BETH

Beth tells the story of an exceptionally resolute, shy, loyal collie in Cumbria. Her master is Todhunter, a fell farmer who is something of a loner, but whose understanding of animals is absolute, and together with Beth he forms a remarkable partnership. In a gesture of revenge against a neighbour, Todhunter uses Beth to steal some of his sheep; soon the two of them are launched on a trail of sheep-rustling in which Beth's ability to anticipate her master's intentions overcomes all practical barriers. In the tight-knit farming community such activities must eventually come to light, and it is in Todhunter's flight north, with Beth at his heels, that disaster strikes, leaving Beth to undertake her last heroic journey. The story does not quite end there, but for the reader much of the fascination of the book lies in its closely-observed picture of the natural world. As well as the remarkable relationship between sheepdog and handler, and an authentic glimpse of how it is achieved, there is the life of the fells which Ernest Lewis had experienced at first-hand: deer-stalking, poaching, fell hunting, hawking, an otter kept for stealing salmon, and above all the interaction of the sheepdog with the flock.

Ernest Lewis was the pen-name of Ernest Vesey, naturalist and sportsman, who died in 1937 at the age of twenty-nine. He wrote four books, all of which drew on his practical sporting experience and his uncanny understanding of animals: *Beth* was written during a stay of several months on the farm of a trainer of sheepdogs in Cumberland.

BETH
A SHEEPDOG

Ernest Lewis

THE BOYDELL PRESS

First published 1934 by Constable & Company Ltd

First published in COUNTRY LIBRARY 1985
by The Boydell Press
an imprint of Boydell and Brewer Ltd
PO Box 9, Woodbridge, Suffolk, IP12 3DF

ISBN 0 85115 242 2

Printed in Great Britain by
St Edmundsbury Press, Bury St Edmunds, Suffolk

AUTHOR'S NOTE

ALTHOUGH this story is simply romance, yet a dog was used to steal sheep, probably very much in the manner described : indeed most of the performances of the different dogs are based on actual facts, and many of them occurred almost exactly as they are told and have only been slightly altered to fit in with the rest of the story.

CONTENTS

CHAPTER I

On a bitter day in the late autumn of the year
18— two men stood talking on the green pack-
horse road, which led from Stonethwaite across
Ridderdale to the lovely village of the lovelier
name, St. Johns-in-the-Vale. Two thousand feet
above them towered the Red Pike, its peak for
the moment hidden in a cloud that drifted across
its face driven by the Helm Wind, the East Wind
which blows deadly cold from off the Pennine
Range ; and in every direction as far as the eye
could see lay the tumbled grandeur of the fells,
all smoky greens and browns and greys.

Both men were similarly clad in grey tweed and
both wore the heavy fell boots weighing seven
pounds the pair, made of the stoutest leather,
with enormously thick soles studded with gigantic
nails, the stoutness to withstand the wear and tear
on the screes and crags and the nails to hold

their footing on the steep fellsides. But, though both men were dressed alike, their professions were clearly shown by the animals which accompanied them.

One, a forester, was holding two magnificent deerhounds, which were coupled together. They stood not less than thirty inches at the shoulder with rough wiry coats, one being slate grey and the other sandy red, but both had black ears and muzzles, and, though everywhere else harsh, the hair on their ears was soft : this peculiarity of their ears showed unmistakably their high breeding. They had the grandest heads, wide high skulls, and long powerful jaws bearded like Vikings, and grand dark eyes that seemed to look upon the world as though they owned it. They showed speed and power in every line, deep narrow chests and wide arched loins, with long galloping quarters enormously muscled up, so that their thighs stood out nearly two inches on each side beyond their hips. Their general conformation was that of large powerful greyhounds, which indeed they were.

These hounds were used for coursing cold harts, deer unwounded by the rifle, and such a course was only possible with hounds of the very highest class, for great speed was necessary to run up to their quarry, while, undistressed, he yet trusted to his turn of foot and great strength to pull him down.

The hooded falcon on the left hand of the other showed him plainly to be a falconer ; at his feet lay stretched a lemon-and-white setter.

" Nay, I seed nowt of her," said Bellis the forester, " when didst th' loss her, Joe ? "

" Yeste'day below t'Mart Crags."

" Didst th' louse her at a groose ? "

" Ai, and Storm t'best falcon that I have be a gay bit." Joe Moore was justifiably depressed for he had been searching for his lost falcon since daylight.

" 'Tis ne'er t'middling hawks I loss, they tak' care o' that, they're flate they might be hungerin', nay, 'tis the gay good 'uns that can catch their ain, and care not if they come yame wi' me or nay."

" Think'st th' that she killed owt ? "

" Ai, ne doubt o' that, but where, that's what I de not ken."

At that moment a man came over the fell breast a quarter of a mile away, riding a pony and followed by a black-and-white sheepdog.

" John Todhunter is a canny way from yame," said Bellis. " I should have thowt he had nowt to fetch him here, I see he has that damn betch with 'un."

" Ai, she's a queer 'un is yon, but a gay good betch on sheep for a' that, 'tis bad for John she's se lame ; fell ower Black Crags was't ? "

" Nay, I canna thowle that, 'twas a stag that gored her sure enow, and serve 'un right, yon's for ever poachin' Sir Ian's deer, but he's too lish for me and though I ken it ower weel I canna catch 'un."

Meanwhile Todhunter approached, and he was a sufficiently striking individual to call for some description : he was a hunchback, and the thin straggling beard failed to conceal the hollow jaws and cadaverous face ; his eyes, very deeply sunk and shadowed by black jutting eyebrows, burnt with an unnatural lustre, and the general effect was that of some dark magician of the fairy stories. He was clad in a shabby coat, corduroy trousers, and clogs, heavy boots with thick wooden soles, the toes bound with brass and the soles and heels shod with iron like a horse.

John Todhunter owed his hunchback to an

accident as a child, and as a result he had suffered
all his life intermittent bouts of pain. These
bouts usually coincided with a change in the
weather, and while he was suffering from one
of them he got little sleep and ate next to nothing ;
he got through somehow the absolutely necessary
work on his small farm and subsisted on vile
cheap whisky, which if taken in sufficiently large
quantities helped to drown his pain. It was
these periods of pain that kept him thin, and it
was easy to tell when he had recently passed
through one, for he was then more ghastly looking and emaciated than ever.

Todhunter's small, wise-looking, rough-
coated Border collie bitch, Fly, was lame of her
back, having been gored in the loin by the brow
antler of a wounded stag that she had brought
to bay. Todhunter took her on all his unlawful
deerstalking operations, but, though she could
be relied upon to bay up a badly wounded deer,
she was too hot and, rushing in, was liable to
be cut before her master could arrive with the
rifle.

As the newcomer rode up the others greeted
him.

" Grand day, John."

" What fettle, John ? "

Todhunter surveyed the bleak grey skies before replying :

" Ai, first rate," but whether he was referring to his health or to the weather was not quite clear.

" I seed a falcon o' thine beyont the hill, Joe," he said.

" Did'st th', where was't ? "

" As I rode be Coldbeck Knotts she waited on ower me for half a mile or more, she turned awa' foreninst t'Clough fold and I last seed 'un ower t'brow."

" Thank the', John, I'm awa'," and Moore went off down the pack-road in the direction whence Todhunter had come : his setter rose and followed him, going singlefoot, the ungainly sidelong pace used by dogs that walk continually at heel.

" Thou'st a lang wa' from yame, John," said Bellis.

" Ai, I'm takin' t'lile betch te Robinson's Bright. Now yon's lame 'tis ower much work for auld Meg, but a brace o' pups from Fly here would set me up gayly well, I reckon. Well, I'll be awa' for I maun be back be milkin' ; 'day, Bob."

" Good-day, John."

Todhunter continued his way down the track and the forester turned north up the hill intending to skirt the Red Pike. The three had scarcely disappeared on their several ways when an old cock grouse came tearing down the wind, hotly pursued by the truant Storm, who was rapidly overhauling him with every clip of her long scythe-like wings. The grouse kept close to the ground but the falcon rose for her stoop and was soon high over her quarry and close behind him. She stooped in great form, flying downwards at a pace which made the grouse appear to be almost standing still ; at the last moment the grouse shifted sideways and avoided the full force of the blow, but nevertheless the falcon cut him hard, and he was knocked almost to the ground in a cloud of feathers. He struggled on, but the falcon, throwing up from her stoop, turned over once more and coming up to him with consummate ease bound to him. They dropped to the ground not a furlong from where the falconer had recently been standing. With one bite the falcon broke the grouse's neck and then started vigorously to plume.

Meanwhile Todhunter and Fly continued on

their way.   Fly, who was then a brilliant bitch, had
at one time been given up as hopeless ; she had
been bred from very good parents and had
the inherited instincts to work sheep and to obey
her handler very strongly developed, indeed the
latter too strongly, for she could stand nothing
in the way of severe treatment which might have
perfectly suited a more sanguine dog.   Her
owner had been a farmer, who being too busy,
or idle, to bother with training dogs, had sent
her to a neighbour of his, Stock.   Stock had a
small farm in Hartsdale and increased his income
as much as possible by training sheepdogs for
other farmers.   As he trained many, time was
of importance to him, and it was his habit to break
his dogs in a string, a method much in use, often
perfectly successful, and far quicker than any
other.

The principle consisted in putting the pup in
a checkcord and by turning him about with the
string, teaching him the various whistles, stop,
go out, come in and left and right.   The string
gave Fly no chance to develop her natural instinct
for sheep, and she disliked the string in itself.
She was in some ways a very wise pup and she
could not understand the twisting and turning

about for no apparent reason. Stock made no attempt to knock her about but he rated her and checked her with the string, and as she was shy and sensitive to command that had more effect upon her than a hiding would have had on many other heavy-headed dogs. She became frightened and her fear completely clogged her intelligence till she appeared sulky and stupid.

Stock persevered with her till from simply a dislike to the string Fly took also a dislike to her trainer, and instead of improving she began to go back. Stock, who had any amount of cheerful easy dogs to train, did not want to bother with a difficult one that would take three or four times as much trouble and only bring him the same money, even if she ever became any good at all, which was by no means certain, and he told Fly's owner that he could do nothing with her.

Todhunter knew Fly's dam, Spy, and he remembered hearing Ridley, her owner, describe a thing which she had once done : Ridley shepherded an enormous piece of fell and some of his sheep fed as much as four miles from his farm ; one day he went to look over his farthest sheep, riding a pony and taking five dogs, one of whom was Spy. The pony was very easy to catch, and, after riding some three miles, when he came to a steep and narrow sheep-trod scarcely safe for a pony, Ridley got off and turned the pony loose, putting the tack under a stone. After walking half a mile or more he missed Spy, but what with having five dogs with him and being busy shepherding he could not be sure where he had seen her last ; he supposed that something had upset her and that she had gone off home for she was a shy bitch, but he was surprised, for she was not a bit sulky and it was not like her to go off and leave him.

Ridley went on with his shepherding and towards evening went on to the next village, then quite close, and spent the night. The next morning he shepherded back a different way and presently came to where he had left his pony. He caught him easily enough and led him by the foretop till he came to the stone where he had left his tack ; when, to his surprise, Spy got up from under the stone and met him. She had been there more than twenty hours, and how long she would have kept her self-appointed watch only she knew.

Todhunter thought that Spy seemed the right sort to breed from and he was also attracted to Fly individually for he had a queer twist in him that made him love all shy wild things, so he bought her for a few shillings. He put a short string on her and led her away home. Fly fought away from the string at every opportunity, and Todhunter knew long before he reached home that she hated the string. When he reached home he took her into his kitchen, where he and all his dogs lived, shut the door and took the string off her. From that time she never wore a string again till her dying day.

For two days Fly lived in the kitchen, Todhunter taking great care that she did not slip out when he went in or out with either of his other dogs. On the third day, thinking that she ought to know him a little or, at any rate, ought to have taken to her new home, he let her come out when he went out to the fell. For a minute she had seemed doubtful about going out, then she went through the door with a rush. It would scarcely be true to say that she had followed him for during the whole time that they were out she rarely came within fifty yards of him, but he was satisfied to find that she hung about, never going much more than a furlong away.

Fly paid no attention to the sheep except once and then she chose the worst possible moment.

Todhunter went on to the high fell and after gathering about a hundred sheep set to work to shed out the hoggs and geld ewes from the lambers. He was anxious to clip his geld sheep, but the lambing ewes were not yet ready, for their new wool was not sufficiently grown. Shedding them out was slow work, for the lambs had got to that age when they cared but little for their mothers or their mothers for them and it was easy to get them separated, and Todhunter had to be very careful that he did not get a ewe that had a lamb in with the geld sheep and leave the lamb amongst the others. It was slow work, for many of the lambs simply refused to mother-up, and hard work, for the geld sheep and lambers stubbornly held together and when shed out fought back to get together once more. After nearly two hours' work it was done, and both the old dogs were well blown and their tongues hanging out. Todhunter had just set Meg to drive the geld ewes and hoggs a little away when Fly, who had all the time been interestedly watching the work from a distance, thought fit to take a hand in the proceedings. She got around the geld sheep, and, as she had naturally a very strong eye and they were only too anxious to get back to the others, they broke at once past Meg and in a moment the whole lot were once more as mixed up as ever. Poor little Fly had no real idea what she was doing, for Stock had scarcely started her on sheep, it was simply her inherited instinct to get around sheep and hold them towards her handler.

Todhunter, seeing that the mischief was already done, called off his other dogs and gently encouraged Fly to fetch the sheep up to him, but that was a mistake, for, as soon as he took notice of her, Fly's shyness returned, and leaving the sheep she went off to a distance and sat down. Todhunter once more shed out his ewes, and drove the geld sheep down to the farm without any further interference from Fly. When he got home Fly was unwilling to go into the house, so Todhunter went in with the other two and left the door open. Presently Fly slipped in on her own.

It was two or three days before Fly would come right up to Todhunter out of doors and a fortnight before she would walk at heel, but once that was achieved they progressed rapidly for a while : being very sensitive to command she soon learnt to stop to the whistle, and she was only too keen to work sheep. She had a grand outrun, wide, and fast, and resolute, got hold of her sheep at once and brought them up quickly and quietly in beautiful style ; but there for a long time her good work ceased ; she would stop to the whistle when on her sheep, but like all strong-eyed dogs she got into that position where she had most command over them and was reluctant to leave it, for she was afraid that that would mean losing her command. It was a long year before she learnt when bidden to go to what she thought the wrong side or to come round quickly between the sheep and her handler or, when shedding, to lie down and let the sheep go by and then at the command come in between ; but once she learnt she was the best shedder in the world, for she would come in like light, straight and hard, and split two sheep however close they hung.

At the finish Fly would do anything, but she was always reluctant to drive away and Todhunter usually let another dog do that when possible. She never quite got over her shyness and would not work so well in the presence of strangers nor would she show her true form if there was another headstrong dog with her that had to be shouted

at or rated. She did not care much for the voice
at all, and Todhunter, who used the voice to a
certain extent for work close at hand, worked
Fly entirely off the whistle : that was doubly
useful, for when the sheep were particularly
stubborn, and at times nothing can be more
tiresome, there was no chance of Todhunter
showing irritation and upsetting Fly, as he might
have done with the voice, for it is hard indeed
to show very much emotion with the whistle
even if one wants to. For all her shyness she
was a particularly powerful forcing bitch on sheep,
and if one wanted to be awkward or charge, she
could stand up to it, aye and go in and meet it
in the face if need be.

Such was Fly the dam of Beth.

CHAPTER II

BRIGHT

ROBINSON'S BRIGHT was, as his owner said, as good a dog as ever ran before a tail, and Robinson had paid a very stiff price for him when he was three years old. Bright was of a very happy, cheery disposition, took to his new master at once and followed him quite willingly, but when Robinson asked him to do any work, Bright simply ignored him and if pressed, left him and went home. At first Robinson did not worry much, for Border collies are often slow in starting work for a new owner, and, as Bright was so good-natured, he felt sure that he would soon start. However, time passed and Bright showed no signs, nor for three months did he do a stroke of work to earn his keep.

Finally Robinson had Bright out one day with two other dogs, a very careful bitch and a puppy; a mob of sheep got jammed in a corner and the other two dogs were quite unable to move them Robinson kept manning them on but the bitch was unable to overcome her natural carefulness and the puppy had not enough experience to do much good. Bright sat watching them, at first thoroughly bored, but he was a very high-class dog and at last he could no longer bear to see the other two making a mess of the job. He got up and went in. He was not only a good dog but a powerful dog, and he shifted the sheep in no time.

From that day Bright always worked quite cheerfully for Robinson, and though it naturally took him a little time to get on to Robinson's commands, which were strange to him, he presently became as good as, or better, than ever. He had enormous resolution and would go almost any distance for sheep : one day Robinson was gathering, as were the farmers who shepherded the fell on each side of him, a thing they did whenever possible for, as their outside sheep ran together if they all gathered at once they would be less likely to miss any. They had almost finished when it blew up misty ; it became impossible to do much more and Robinson, after sending out Bright to fetch a few sheep which he knew to be close at hand, decided simply to look through those that he had already, and then go home. Bright was a surprisingly long time out and finally, instead of coming with the eight or ten that Robinson had wanted, arrived with over two hundred.

In the mist Bright had passed quite close to the sheep he had been sent for, but did not see them, and went straight on till he heard the flock which Allen, Robinson's neighbour, had gathered. In spite of Allen's abuse and the efforts of his two dogs Bright took hold of the sheep, and away with them back to his master leaving Allen alone with his dogs.

*   *   *   *   *

About midday Todhunter came to the village of Ashness-in-Morsdale, he passed through the village and rode about a mile down Morsdale. Robinson's was the fourth farm beyond the village ; each farm had a few acres of enclosed and fairly fertile land around, while behind them stretched the almost limitless expanse of fell where their sheep grazed. Todhunter, on his arrival, was directed to put his pony and bitch together into a barn while he went in to dinner. After dinner they went out to see Bright run.

Robinson slightly opened the door of a lean-to shed, or as he called it " dog-hole," when six or eight dogs immediately made a rush to get out ; Robinson thrust his knee into the opening saying :

" Get in, ye beggars, get in."   Then after a moment,

" Come on, Nell—Bright—Jed."

Nell was a smooth-coated black-and-white bitch rather thick and short on the leg.   Bright, a black-and-tan rough-coated dog, was tall, lathy and lightly made ; he had drooping ears, a fine muzzle and a slightly dished face ; in general build he was on lines of speed, and was not unlike a lurcher except for his long thick coat and bushy tail.   Jed was also rough-coated and black-and-tan, but she showed a good deal more white than Bright, she was smaller and thicker built but seemed ungainly and puppyish ; Robinson pointing to her said :

" Jed there is got be Bright, she is nobbut seven months but is shaping gayly well and shows grand style."

The two men walked up a narrow lane that led up behind the house to the fell.   The dogs raced and played about but never went more than fifty yards from their master.   They came out of the lane into the fell-intake where there were a few heavy-horned tups. Jed ran off in their direction but Robinson called her in with :

" That'll do, Jed, that'll do there, come in."

Before they reached the top of the intake two old tups started to fight, for it was their rutting season : they drew about thirty yards apart and charged each other like knights at a tourney ; they met with a fearful crack that could be heard for yards, once more drew off and charged again with unabated fury. Four times they repeated their shattering charges, before one of them, evidently finding he was getting the worst of it, gave up and cleared off. They remained always head to head and backed away after the charge so that each gave his opponent no chance to take a mean advantage and charge him unbeknown in the hinder parts. Sometimes as they met their hindquarters flew up in the most comical manner, for the force of the collision was terrific and left no doubt as to the origin of the battering ram.

Robinson paid little or no attention to the contest but he pointed out a black-faced Swaledale tup that he said a few days before had killed a Wensleydale which he had got for crossing on

some of his Swaledale and Herdwick ewes.   The
Swaledale tup had jumped over the wall out of the
intake then, forcing his way through a hedge, had
got in with the Wensleydale.   The Wensleydale
tups have no horns and by meeting in a head-on
charge the heavy armoury of the other, this
unfortunate scion of his race had broken his neck.

Robinson and Todhunter went through the
gate in the intake wall on to the fell proper ;
pointing to a breast half a mile away Robinson
said :

"There'll be some sheep ower yon brow, I'll
let him run and have a lake what he can fetch."

He called the three dogs in, and then, with a
scarcely perceptible flick of the fingers of his
left hand, said in a quiet conversational voice :

"Bright."

Bright shot out on Robinson's left side and
raced away half-left at the top of his speed.

While Bright is making his outrun let us get
to know Robinson's commands, for he worked
his dogs entirely on the voice except for a stop
whistle.

"Come bye," was go left, "Here to me," go
right, "Way out," meant go farther out, and
"Come in," the opposite, and "Drive on," walk

up to his sheep. Besides these he had a few different commands for Nell that he might the easier work them together, Nell's commands were : " Go on," for left, " Get back," for right, and " Fetch on " for walk up to her sheep. The others were the same as Bright's.

After going some three hundred yards, Bright saw some sheep on his left which were hidden from the shepherds by a swell in the ground, and he cast farther away to that side to get around them.

Robinson blew his whistle.

Bright stopped at once and looked round.

" Way out, Bright," Robinson shouted " way out."

Bright paid no more attention to the sheep, but set off once more straight up the fell. After going about three furlongs, evidently thinking that he was far enough, he began to swing in to his right. Robinson stopped him with the whistle, and as Bright looked round, Robinson took a couple of paces to his left shouting :

" Wa-a-ay out. Wa-a-ay out."

Bright turned back at once, continued his original half-left course, and in a moment disappeared from view over the breast of the fell. About three minutes later a dozen Swaledale shearlings came into view over the brow a couple of hundred yards to the right of where Bright had disappeared. A moment later Bright came into sight behind them and brought them quickly up.

When the sheep were within about two hundred yards of him Robinson called, not loudly, " Come bye " and then as Bright swung to the left he whistled.

Bright stopped to the left rear of the sheep.

" Drive on."

Bright walked up to his sheep and drove them diagonally to his right across Robinson's front

" Here to me."

Bright raced around to his right and got into his original position behind his sheep. " Here to me," and he was at the right-hand corner where he was stopped by the whistle.

" Drive on."

Bright drove the sheep diagonally to his left.

Robinson then put him back behind the sheep so that they were being driven once more straight towards him. As the sheep came up to him Robinson said :

" Come here to me a bit, Bright. Come here to me a bit."

Bright edged a little over to his right and drove

the sheep past Robinson to his right. He seemed a little inclined to keep outside them and Robinson said again :

" Come here to me a bit."

When the sheep were well behind him Robinson said :

" Come bye, Come bye."

Then as soon as Bright had gone out left-handed till he was opposite the sheep and at right angles to his old course, Robinson stopped him by hissing through his teeth and then said :

" Drive on."

Bright drove the sheep straight past and behind Robinson.

"Come bye." Then a hiss and then "Drive on."

Bright brought the sheep once more past Robinson and drove them straight away to Robinson's front. After he had gone maybe a hundred yards,

" Here to me.   Here to me."

Bright, paradoxically enough, went by right-handed till, instead of being between his master and the sheep, he was beyond them and on the command " Drive on," brought them back.

" Here to me, Here to me, Here to me," in an urgent voice.

Bright raced round and round right-handed outside his sheep then as he passed behind them, Robinson stopped him with the whistle, and once more gave the order " Drive on."

As Todhunter saw Bright race around the sheep he said :

" Ai, but yon's verra easy te move."

" Ai, he's that," Robinson agreed, " but I de not do ower much o' yon stuff wi' 'un, he'd verra soon be wasted, but I was keen to show thee what 'un is."

" Ai, yon's a gay good dog, ne doubt o' that."

When the sheep were almost up to Robinson, he hissed and Bright lay down.

Robinson then put a string on to Jed and gave her to Todhunter to hold, then holding out his right hand he said :

" Nell get back."

Nell went out on his right, as soon as she was opposite the sheep on their flank Robinson whistled.

Nell lay down.

" Fetch on."

Nell got up and walked slowly and carefully towards the sheep, while Bright, who paid not the slightest attention to Nell's orders, lay motionless, just following them with his eyes as they moved out between him and Robinson on Robinson's left.

As the tail sheep came opposite to Bright, Robinson hissed and as Nell stopped and lay down he said, " Go on."

Nell raced around to her left behind Robinson and came up in the face of the sheep.

Robinson hissed, and Nell lay down.

" Bright come in steady."

Bright got up and walked in two or three paces, and then lay down to the hiss.

" Fetch on."

Nell got up and walked in towards her sheep. As the sheep began to move between him and Bright, Robinson hissed and Nell lay down.

As the sixth sheep went past him, Robinson pointed to the narrow gap between her and the seventh saying, " Bright this."

Bright leaped to his feet and dashed in, dropping as though shot the instant that the seventh sheep turned back.

Robinson took a couple of paces backwards, saying the while " Fetch on."

Nell got up and almost immediately dropped again as Robinson hissed.

The six remaining sheep filed through between Bright and Robinson, and as the last one came up he said once more, " Bright this."

Bright shot in and cut the sheep off from the others, but she did not like to be alone and tried to break by to the rest. Robinson pointed to her, saying, " Here this, this, this," and Bright leaped this way and that always in front of the exceedingly active shearling as she made determined efforts to rejoin her companions, but it was in vain, she could not get by and Bright wore her right up to his master.

Presently Robinson said, "That'll do."

Bright came round to heel and Nell got up and walked to him, while the shearling dashed off after the others.

Robinson took Jed from Todhunter, saying :

" Let's lake what this lile beggar can de," and took the string off her. He paid no heed to her till the sheep had roamed some little distance away, then he said :

" Jed come in ahint," and as the pup came in to heel, he held out his right hand level with his shoulder, saying :

" Jed gow 'way."

Jed raced away on the right of the sheep, but

too close to them and Robinson stopped her with the whistle.

Jed lay down and looked back over her shoulder.

Robinson walked out to his right, saying :

" Jed get out, ssht, ssht, ssht, ssht, get out."

The pup got up and went on making a bit wider sweep to her right, but still quite close enough; however, she got round behind her sheep into a position where she had good command and then lay down watching them.

Robinson turned to Todhunter, saying :

" Yon's a straight-necked beggar, but she'll come till in time, and she's got a grand folly on, watch 'un now. Fetch on, Jed, good lass, Jed, fetch on, Jed, fetch on."

Jed got up and slowly and carefully drove the sheep in towards her master.

" There, is't yon ne bonny style, see'st the' the way she arches her back, and crouches on her shoulders, and head right down, just like t'auld dog, and her tail, too, right on her hocks, yon's what I like te see, an a dog raises 'un's tail it shows verra weel he's wrong o't'head."

As the sheep came up to Robinson Jed lay down and watched them.

Robinson made an almost imperceptible sign to Bright, who just moved the sheep off to the left, then he hissed and Bright lay down.

Jed watched them alert and eager and scarcely waited for the " Jed get back " before she was once more around them ; she got into a position of command and lay down.

"That'll do, Jed, that'll do; come in, lass, that'll do."

Jed got up with evident reluctance and came round towards her master, but, as she came by and the sheep started to move away, she stopped and half-turned to go around them once more, but Robinson called again, just the least bit sharply.

" That'll do, Jed, that'll do there," and then, as she came in, more quietly, " Come in lass, good lass Jed, come in."

They went back to the farm and presently Todhunter set off on his ride home. Robinson would take no service fee, but it was agreed that Todhunter should pay him a small fee if Fly had living pups and that he should give Robinson a pup.

Todhunter said that he should have the pick of the dogs, as he himself only used bitches.

CHAPTER III

WANCHEATE FARM

As Todhunter came back over Ridderdale in the evening he noticed the scattered feathers where the falcon had made her meal. He rode over and looked at the remains and saw that Storm had eaten the greater part of the grouse and as well as eating the head and neck had bitten great pieces out of the breastbone, a sure sign that it was a hawk's work.

Todhunter rode through Stonethwaite and took a track that followed the Scarsdale Beck. After going a mile or more beyond the village he came to Joe Moore's cottage. In answer to his hail, Moore shouted to him to come in. Todhunter hung his pony's rein on the gate, and, followed by Fly, walked into the kitchen.

Moore, who was busy imping a feather in a tiercel's wing, said :

" Sit the' down, John, I'll be done wi' this lile chappy in a moment."

The hawk, which was hooded, was lying on his breast on a cushion on the kitchen table with a piece of linen over his back, and Mrs. Moore was holding him still by pressing him tightly down on to the cushion. The falconer had cut off a broken flight feather with a razor just below the break and was cutting a moulted feather, which he had selected from a pile at his elbow, to take the place of the broken part. Then he took an imping needle from a saucer of salt and water and thrust it for half its length into the quill of the new feather and the other end into the quill in the hawk's wing, set the feather square, and thrust it home. It fitted so well that, except for the bars of colour on the feathers, it was almost impossible to tell that it was not the hawk's own feather. In a little while the salt water would slightly rust the needle and weld the pieces of feather firmly together. Moore let the hawk up and took him on his hand, stroking him gently till he should settle down and recover from his fright.

" Didst see owt o' thy falcon, Joe ? " Todhunter asked.

" Nay, she maun ha' moved afore I got there, and fed I am wi' lakin' for 'un."

" She killt a groose on Ridderdale for I seed t'pelt, but nowt o' t'falcon."

" Was't hawk killt groose, think'st the' ? "

" Ai, I ken verra weel 'twas yane, the way 'twas ate, but maybe 'twere no thine."

" Nay, 'twas she sure enow, and I'll have t' lile divil now, I'm ne flate she'll go ower far on a full crop, she'll jouke on t'Red Pike, and I'll have her in t'morning. Thank the', Joe, for tellin' me."

" Nay, ne trouble, but I maun be awa' noo."

" Nay, thou'lt stop for a sup o' tay afore thou goest, Mr. Todhunter," put in Mrs. Moore, " t' will ne be a shake."

" Nay, thank the', Mrs. Moore, I maun be back te t'milkin'. Good day te the', 'day, Joe."

After leaving the falconer's cottage the track became very ill-defined for it led only to Wancheate Farm where Todhunter lived ; as a rule he only used it once a week when he took his butter and eggs into Stonethwaite and returned with any provisions that he needed for himself, and few people ever came out to the farm from the village. The track continued along the right-hand bank of the Scarsdale Beck, between the beck and the fellside of Hellaw : on the other side of the beck rose Blenthorpe Fell. The country was very desolate and wild, and, as Todhunter rode farther from Stonethwaite, the fells on each side seemed to close in upon him. The side of Hellaw, which at first sloped fairly gently down to the beckside, became steeper and steeper till it towered above him in a precipitous wall of screes and crags fifteen hundred feet high. Blenthorpe also became more desolate and the tough fell grass gave way to stunted heather and then to blaeberry wire, lady's mantle, stagshorn and lichens, and finally to a tumbled mass of screes, shale, and crags, cut across by deep gills, and only here and there could a small patch of dark ling find a precarious foothold amongst the crags.

Presently the fellside took a turn to the right and the end of Hellaw stood silhouetted, a mighty buttress against the sky: for the top two hundred feet it fell in a sheer cliff of shining black granite, and then more gently, but still roughly enough, to the level of the beck. Once past the corner Lake Southermere, into which the Scarsdale Beck flowed, could be seen half a mile away.

Todhunter's farm lay between Hellaw on the north, Lake Southermere on the south-west,

and the Scarsdale Beck on the south-east ;
and it was thus peculiarly fenced in by the nature
of the ground. Lake Southermere, which lay
roughly north and south, was some seven miles
long and varied in width from half a mile to
two miles : the Scarsdale Beck flowed into it
about three miles from its northern end. The
beck at times raced over and around enormous
boulders, but in the places where it flowed more or
less smoothly it was rarely less than three feet
deep and after much rain sometimes as much
as twice that depth ; it everywhere flowed at a
great pace and there was no bridge nearer than
Stonethwaite. Hellaw rose up to the north
of the farm in a swelling breast, scattered with
enormous boulders, and in places so steeply
that a man could scarcely keep his footing except
on the narrow sheep-trods. The granite cliff,
called the Black Crags, ran along the top of the
fell from the beckside to the lake's edge, it
varied in height from fifty to three hundred
feet, and was everywhere quite unscalable
except in one place where the Wancheate Gill
broke through it. On the lakeside the southern
part of Hellaw fell almost sheer into the water
in a great cliff known as the Eagle Crags ;

for the cliff was one of the last English strong-
holds of the golden eagle. There were three
several eyries, great untidy heaps of sticks and
heather six feet or more across the base, and to
one or other of these nests a pair of eagles
annually returned and reared their young, they
had done so since no man knew when or, as the
hillmen tersely put it, " always."

The only possible land approaches to the farm
were up the track by the beckside, or down off
the top of Hellaw by way of the Wancheate
Gill and the latter was a path which could only
be taken by a sheep or an active man who was
not affected by heights. The farm was made
even more desolate-looking by the barren north
side of Blenthorpe, for it was practically all screes
and crags to its top, the Great Rigg. Once
over the Rigg it swelled out more gently and
offered good pasturage for sheep, but sheep
rarely wandered on to the north side.

Apart from its lonely situation Wancheate was
not considered a desirable farm ; the few acres
of enclosed land by the lakeside were rough, poor
pasturage, and furthermore the farm was stocked
with sheep almost up to its full capacity. Fell
sheep have a very strongly developed homing

instinct ; they will return enormous distances to their own heath, the place where they were suckled, and thirty miles is by no means an unknown distance for a fell sheep to return home. Even when they are prevented by fences or by the nature of the country from taking the direct route back, they will fight and fight towards their heaths, and if possible overcome or go round any obstacle. This homing instinct is extremely useful on the fells where there are no fences, and keeps the sheep pretty well in their own district, but it cuts both ways for it prevents sheep being sold to neighbouring farmers, and very nearly all the sheep sold off the fells go to enclosed country or to the butcher ; and it can also be very tiresome if a sheep adopts some unauthorised home of her own.

Todhunter had had one ewe that as a three-year-old he meant to draft in the autumn, but whenever he brought her down she jumped out and returned to the high fell, and finally when the buyer came she was not to be found. The next spring she came into the fields by the farm along with the others to lamb and presently was put out once more to the fell. But then she decided that she preferred the mowing fields to the fell, and, as often as she was put out, returned and jumped into one of the hayfields. She was a Herdwick, always thick, stocky sheep compared with the more active Swaledales, and Jemima, as Todhunter christened her, was a particularly solid old lady, but she was well able to deal with the walls, and her lamb inherited or acquired the same capacity.

Todhunter turned Jemima out so often that she got to know him, and would try and hide in a corner of one of the fields when she saw him coming, and when discovered would look at him in the most comical manner. When being driven away from the farm, it was like pulling teeth to get her along at all, and if she saw an opportunity when he was not looking she would whip out of sight behind a stone, and her lamb was as quick as she. Todhunter several times took her right up on to the top of Hellaw, but Jemima was always back in the mowing by evening. One day he took her up by way of the beckside and left her on the top of Hellaw ; he was an hour or more looking over the other sheep up there, and went down the near way by the Wancheate Gill. As he came down through the Black Crags, he saw Jemima paddling

away down across the lower breast below him
with her lamb following along behind. She
was not hurrying but never stopping, and, with
head up, was going at a good steady determined
pace. As Todhunter overtook her Jemima saw
him and got off the track and out of sight among
the rocks, but, as soon as he was gone on, she
came on into her hayfield.

After that Todhunter's annoyance gave way
to a kind of amused affection, and he left her to
do as she liked, and as soon as the hay was cut
she went off up to the fell on her own.

When, as incoming tenant, Todhunter took
over Wancheate Farm he, as was usual, took with
it a certain number of sheep, and when he gave up
the farm he would have to leave a like number
of similar sheep for the next tenant. These
sheep, in fact, really belonged to the landlord,
they were useful to give Todhunter a start, as
he could breed a stock of his own from them,
but as the farm would not maintain many more
than the number of sheep taken over he had no
chance to increase the stock, but had to keep
selling off as they came.

There were two heaths on Wancheate Farm,
one on the breast below the Black Crags, and the

other on top of Hellaw itself.   On coming into
the farm Todhunter had taken over two hundred
gimmer, or female, sheep ; of these one hundred
and twenty belonged to the lower heath, and
eighty to the upper. Hellaw could have fed
without difficulty a thousand sheep, or ten
thousand, for most of the year, but the squire,
Sir Ian Stuart, preserved the greater part of it
for a deer forest and grouse moor. Sheep
and shepherding not only disturbed the deer,
but sheep could often spoil what might otherwise
have been a most successful stalk, for few deer
need to hear twice the whistling snort of a startled
sheep before they are off : and it was laid down
in the lease that Todhunter might not keep more
than one hundred sheep on the upper heath,
exclusive of lambs running on their dams.
The lower heath, being circumscribed and
not very good pasture, could not properly
feed many more than one hundred and fifty
sheep.

The farmhouse was little more than a cabin
one story high and with only two principal rooms ;
however, it was warm and dry, for the large stones
that made its thick walls were all water-set, set
sloping downwards and outwards, and the huge

rough slates in the roof were many of them nearly an inch thick.

At the yard gate Todhunter took the saddle and bridle off his pony, who promptly lay down for a good roll before wandering off to feed. Todhunter took the saddle and bridle with him into the kitchen, the door of which he had not troubled to lock in his absence. As he came in a Border bitch, Meg, walked over to him slowly waving her bushy tail in greeting. He threw his tack into a corner saying, " 'llo, Meg," and walked over to a heap of deerskins from which an otter rather surprisingly lifted his short round face. Todhunter leaned down and scratched him behind an ear with a lean forefinger, saying,

" Well, thou lile beggar, what hast the' been at ? "

But the otter simply curled up once more and went to sleep. It was not a very cordial reception but the best of which the otter was capable, and had there been anyone with Todhunter, the otter would have been through the half-open door and into the next room long before they were even in the kitchen.

Todhunter had dug his otter out of a holt as a cub and had hoped to use him for catching

salmon and trout, but, though he was a perfect
natural poacher, he was not always easy to work ;
he was tame enough with Todhunter, would follow
him like a dog and come back to him when called,
and yet he was so shy with strangers that he would
clear off and hide as soon as he saw or heard
anyone. So there was no risk of Todhunter
being caught poaching with him ; but he had a
nasty trick when he had caught a fish of slipping
out quietly on the opposite bank, getting under
a stone or bush and eating it. Sometimes if
the beck was full, which it usually was when the
salmon were up, the otter could get out un-
observed and eat a good deal before he was found;
if he managed to swallow a certain amount the
day's poaching was over, for the otter would not
work on a full stomach.

Besides, he could only be worked when he was
in a good temper, which was by no means always
the case, though Todhunter learned to tell by
his actions, whether he whistled or snorted or
growled. Todhunter probably got more pleasure
than profit from his poaching, for when his otter
was in real form and the water was clear he
showed great sport in the beck. He was never
tried in the lake for fear of losing him.

Todhunter relit the fire, which had gone out, stacked it up with peat and went out to attend to his three shorthorn cows and two heifers in the byre.

Two days after his visit to Robinson, Todhunter went up on to the fell to gather his sheep for the autumn dipping. He took both Meg and Fly and set off up the Wancheate Gill through the Crag Gate on to the top of Hellaw ; it was no great distance but it was a steep, rough track and took him the greater part of an hour to come out on the top ; from there there was a magnificent view in nearly every direction over the fells. The tops of some of the higher fells were in the clouds, and it was a beautiful sight as the mists wreathed past the peaks and in and out of the gills. Todhunter, however, paid no attention for he had seen it all too often before, but he stood for a moment to watch an eagle soaring in wide effortless rings, his six-foot span of wing spread to the utmost and every flight feather extended. He apparently never moved his wings, but he tilted himself one way and another to catch the flaws of wind. Fly, who was routing about, put up a hare ; the eagle saw her and banked majestically over, still without flapping his wings, and then, bending them somewhat at the elbow, he glided away in pursuit. He was only slightly descending and made no effort to assist the force of gravity, yet he rapidly overtook the hare ; he passed quite close to Todhunter, who plainly heard the sough of his wings, a softer note than the screaming hiss of the stooping falcon. As the eagle came up to the hare, she turned sharply about in her track and completely threw the eagle out. The eagle, realising that further pursuit was hopeless, gave up and flapped heavily away ; as soon as he began to flap his wings all his majesty was gone and nothing could have been more ungainly. Yet after a few strokes he took once more to the soar, and by simply making use of the currents of air regained his former majestic pitch.

Todhunter turned to his right and walked along not far from the edge of the fell. He sent Fly to gather any sheep between him and the cliff and Meg to get those on his left. He went on till he could see down to the Scarsdale Beck, and then turned back to his left, going parallel to his old route, but farther from the cliff. When he came opposite the Crag Gate, he stopped and made Meg drive the sheep down along the gill

towards the cliff : then he whistled her in, went
on, and gathered out to the Eagle Crags and
back. He picked up the first lot of sheep and
went down the Crag Gate to the farm below.

Throughout, all that Todhunter had done
had been to walk out right and left of Crag
Gate and give the various whistles to his dogs,
who had done all the work, gathering sometimes
half a mile or more away from him. Todhunter
could not whistle on his fingers but used a home-
made whistle which was simply a doubled piece
of tin about an inch square, the open end being
slightly bent down and the two tips opened out
about a quarter of an inch apart, and a hole bored
through the centre of both halves. This whistle
was better than any bought one for it could blow
any note the same as on the fingers.

Todhunter put the sheep in one of the fields
by the farm while he got his dinner. In the
afternoon he put them all through the dip :
dipping was really two men's work, one to dip and
the other to hand the sheep to him, but Fly almost
took the place of the second man, for she was so
powerful that she forced the sheep right up to
Todhunter where he stood beside the dip ; still
it was hard work for all three of them.

Todhunter left the sheep in the pasture for the night and the next day renewed their wool-marks. The high-fell sheep had a mark down the near ribs and another on the near shoulder ; the mark was made with a mixture of tar and red. There was also an ear mark, crop near and fork on far, that is, a piece was cut off the end of the near ear and the fork was cut in the tip of the far ear. These ear marks were made with the shears before the lambs were first turned out to fell with their dams, and lasted for life. Then he shed out the wether shearlings, and a few old ewes that he intended to sell to a wholesale buyer who made the rounds of the farms in the autumn. From the rest Todhunter shed out the other ewes and big gimmer shearlings and put them in a field where, on about the first of November, he would loose the tups to them. The rest, consisting of hoggs and a few small gimmer shearlings, he turned out on to the fell bottom. Most of these had made their way up through Crag Gate on to their heath before morning.

The next day Todhunter gathered out his sheep from the fell below the cliff : to do that dogs were not only useful but absolutely necessary, for the sheep got into places amongst the crags where a man could not safely go without a rope, but Meg and Fly went up after them and drove them out, though sometimes not without difficulty. When the whole flock had been collected a few were found of the high-fell sheep that had not returned to their heath from the night before and two others that had wandered down at some time and so had missed being dipped with the others. Those of the upper heath that had been dipped but had not returned were shed out and left behind, but the others were taken down and treated in the same way as the first lot. The sheep from the lower fell had a bugle horn wool mark on the far side, a red mark running from the root of the tail up the back and down over the far ribs ; and their ear marks were lower half near, and upper key cut far—a square piece cut out of the lower corner of the near ear and a square piece cut with a key out of the top side of the far ear.

As he marked the sheep, Todhunter counted them, for the spring and autumn dippings and the summer clipping were the only times when the sheep were counted.

He missed an old ewe out of the lower-fell

sheep which he knew should have been there ; she might possibly have met with an accident, as falling over a crag or the like, or wandered away, but most likely she had simply been left behind in the crags. Todhunter did not expect to find all his sheep at the first gathering, but always went around again at least once to get any that had been missed, and indeed it was nothing wonderful for him to find a rough sheep two or three weeks after he had thought that he had clipped them all, and that although he was continually amongst his sheep. Todhunter very rarely knew exactly how many sheep he had and might easily miss half a dozen or more and not notice it, unless, as in this case, there was one amongst them that he particularly expected to see ; for all that, he knew his own sheep when he saw them and could tell one from another easily enough ; apart from their general appearance he distinguished them more particularly by their faces, the set of their heads and necks, and their walk.

CHAPTER IV

BETH'S EARLY DAYS

A LITTLE before Christmas Fly's puppies were born. Shortly before she was due, Todhunter made her a bed in the room off the kitchen where he himself slept ; then, by keeping the connecting door shut and opening the door out of the bed-room, he was able to give Fly complete liberty, and at the same time keep Meg and the otter shut in when he wanted.

Fly had five pups, two bitches and three dogs ; when they were a few days old Todhunter drowned two of the dogs, for he only wanted the two bitches for himself and one dog for Robinson and he did not want anyone else to get hold of his good blood, besides which he thought Fly could do the three better and more easily than five, especially as she had never carried much flesh since the wound in her loin. As soon as the puppies were born, and indeed for a little time before, Todhunter took care to give Fly all that she would eat, for in some ways sheepdogs have much of the wild animal about them and there was a risk that if Fly, while suckling her pups and running loose, did not get enough food to do them well she might help herself and get into some mischief.

The worst time was just when Fly was weaning her pups, for Todhunter let her do it herself ; she had a passion for getting bits of food and burying them, she stole anything she could get hold of but mostly eggs, she raided the henhouses several times a day and though Todhunter did his best to get there first, Fly did everything but sit and wait for the hens to lay. In ordinary times Fly would never dream of taking an egg, so Todhunter did not beat her for it when she was only doing it for her pups.

Luckily Fly did nothing worse than take eggs and dig up the most horrible and smelly morsels and bring them in to her pups, nothing to be compared with the crime once committed by an old bitch Mirl.

At the time when Mirl was weaning her pups Todhunter had had an old blind ewe who lived happily in the garden, or what had been a garden before Todhunter's reign, for then it was only a small grass paddock with a few unkept gooseberry bushes and surrounded by a wall. The blind ewe had just lambed and was feeling a bit sick so Mirl stole the new-born lamb without her ever being aware of it and Todhunter caught her taking it in to the pups. She carried it very gently and it was quite unhurt and perhaps Mirl had some dim idea of entering her pups to live game. Lamb stealing was the worst possible sin and Todhunter realised that Mirl should have a frightful hiding. He went in to her with a big stick and made it clear that he was going to hide her, so Mirl did not wait for him and Todhunter only made the most half-hearted pretence at catching her and was glad when he missed her, for he could not forget that she had been doing her best for her pups.

Todhunter returned the lamb to its mother, who was beginning to search anxiously for it, and Mirl kept out of his way for the rest of the afternoon, so no one was any the worse and she never took another lamb.

As soon as he was old enough to go, Todhunter got Robinson to come over for his dog pup, and got him out of the way. The bitch pups,

Beth and Jess, when they were little more than two months old began to show signs of eye and style ; they started to play at being sheepdogs, practising on the hens and ducks in the yard ; they would, as they got older, round up a few into a corner and then lie and watch them, and if any sheep came into the yard they showed great excitement.

When she was about three months old Beth first showed a sign of what she was later to become. Todhunter went out with Meg and Fly to look over a few sheep that he had in one of the enclosed pastures, and the two pups followed him : he paid no heed to them and presently climbed a wall that was too big for them. Todhunter went on with Meg and Fly and supposed that the pups would go home. An hour later he came back by a different way and noticed Jess lying basking in the yard and never thought but that Beth was about somewhere ; but an hour or two later when he still saw no sign of her he began to call her and, when she did not come, he went off to look for her. When he came to the place where he had got over the wall he found Beth curled up beneath it sound asleep ; being asleep on sentry duty rather spoilt the effect, but perhaps it was too much to expect the little beggar to keep awake for nearly three hours on end. When Todhunter came up to her she jumped up as pleased as Punch and apparently had never doubted that he would come back. After that Beth was always something of a Casabianca and Todhunter had to watch that it did not get her into trouble.

After a while the pups made life such a misery for the hens and ducks, and generally got a bit above themselves, so Todhunter kept them shut up in the kitchen unless he was about himself ; and that was the more necessary as the first week in April he fetched the lambing ewes down into the enclosures around his farm. Once the pups were old enough to do any mischief he took care that they were never out of doors out of his sight, particularly if they were together. If ever he missed one he searched unceasingly till he had found her, for he knew the adage :

> The Devil will
> Find mischief still
> For idle hands to do

applied most pertinently to sheepdog puppies. Their natural instinct was to herd sheep and it was a small step for a green and keen puppy who had not the speed or confidence to run wide of her sheep, from herding to chasing, and then from chasing to gripping, and thence, possibly, even to worrying.

Between the ages of about three and six months Todhunter took the pups out with him when he went around the sheep as long as he was not going far enough to tire them. If possible, he never took more than one of the pups at a time, for one by herself with one or both of the old bitches paid more attention to him and thought less of play. At that time he paid little attention to them, but he gradually taught them to walk in at heel when bidden, stop to the whistle and lie down. They learnt easily enough, for they had hundreds of generations of obedience and training behind them, but he taught them the more gently on account of that and took care not to frighten them in any way. If they wanted to do any work on sheep on their own, which they soon began to do, he let them be as long as they worked gently ; if they showed signs of doing wrong he did not rate them but simply called them in.

CHAPTER V

GEORGE DOBSON, POACHER

BETH inherited all her mother's shyness and, as few people came out to the farm, she was even shyer with strangers than she might otherwise have been : the otter, too, set her a bad example by always slipping into the inner room whenever anyone came, and Beth got into the habit of going with him, or otherwise hiding while anyone strange was about. Todhunter, if anything, really rather liked this shyness, and he made no attempt to break her of it. Practically the only people who ever came to the farm were Moore and Bellis, and, more rarely, the under-forester Patterson, whose lawful business sometimes brought them to the southern end of Hellaw, and George Dobson, whose unlawful business brought him there still more often.

Dobson was a professional poacher, he was the son of a small farmer, but he never did any farming himself. He took the right over a small, poor shoot that he might have a lawful right to sell his game, but little, indeed, of the game that he sold came off his own shoot. He was a brilliant shot and once backed himself to shoot twenty-nine out of thirty rabbits bolted by ferrets. He won his bet. He was a great runner and he laughed at the keepers, for they could never catch him, however close they might get to him.

Many were the tales told of Dobson's exploits and of those of his two dogs who were scarcely less clever than himself : they were a red setter bitch, Fan, and a lurcher, Jack. Fan was probably the most remarkable. The keepers, realising that it was next to impossible to catch Dobson in the open, tried to lay an ambush for him at his cottage and catch him as he returned from his nightly excursions, but Fan learnt to go on in front when Dobson got near home and would make the round of the cottage. If she winded a keeper she would come back to Dobson, but if all was clear she would go and lie down on the doorstep until he came up.

One evening, when Dobson went into the Blue Boar Inn at Stonethwaite, Taylor, the head keeper, was already in the bar and was engaged in a more or less heated argument with the innkeeper on the merits of two trail hounds, both of which had a big reputation in the district. Fan, who was with Dobson, knew Taylor well enough and she was used to making herself as inconspicuous as possible, so she slipped quietly in under the bench unnoticed by either of the other two. Dobson ordered a drink and Taylor, changing the subject off trail hounds, began to chaff Dobson, saying that he might be a " terrible lish fellow enow " but that sooner or later he would catch him.

Dobson said little, but he presently pointed out to Fan a hare that the keeper had laid close to his legs. He did not speak to her, for at his business silence was important and his dogs worked a good deal from signs. As soon as he felt Fan move along under the bench Dobson began to run down the trail hound that Taylor had been cracking up as he came in. During the ensuing argument Fan got hold of the hare, slipped out of the door, and away with her home, the hare in her mouth.

Presently Taylor got up to go home, and looked for his hare, when lo ! it was gone. The innkeeper remembered having seen it lying there, while Dobson denied having seen it at all and offered the suggestion, which was not well received, that the hare had probably only been stunned, and had got up and gone off unbeknown to them. Taylor was quite certain in his own mind that Dobson had got hold of the hare somehow, but he could not for the life of him think how, for Dobson had never left the bar since coming in and his pockets were most convincingly empty. The mystery of the missing hare was never properly cleared up.

The lurcher, Jack, though possibly not so wise as Fan, was very smart on rabbits. Once Alan McDonald, the squire's brother-in-law, was walking through the Manor Park with Valour and Courage, his two fighting dogs, Staffordshire pit bull terriers, though they were sufficiently unlike the show white bull terrier ; they had short, round, powerful faces and neither of them weighed more than twenty-five pounds, but they were almost perfect examples of strength and quickness in a small space, and were almost impossible to knock off their feet. The dog, Valour, was brindled with a little white, and the bitch, Courage, was fawn and white. Though their ears had been clipped as pups, they had never been fought, and their owner had always taken great care to prevent them doing so. At one time Courage had always run from a big dog, but one day she had been set upon by a big cur nearly four times her weight before she had seen it. She cried and made every effort to get away, but finding she could not, she stopped crying and started fighting. In spite of the combined efforts of three people the cur was dead before they could be separated. Courage never ran from that day but she was still just as quiet as ever. McDonald had got them for boars which were fairly common where he had lived in New Zealand.

When out boarhunting he took two or three crossbred hounds and the fighting dogs. The hounds would find and presently bay up a boar. Valour and Courage, if they were not actually with them at the time, would very soon arrive and without hesitation go in to the boar's throat together, one at each side. The angry old boar would lunge left or right at one of them, who would check just out of range, while the other on the other side would go in to the boar's exposed throat. Immediately he or she got a hold the boar thrust that side, and the other one

got a hold on the other side.   Then both lay back
on their haunches and pulled apart.

McDonald arrived as best he could, got
behind the boar and, taking him by the hind-
legs, turned him on to his back and, while Valour
and Courage still holding on on each side kept
him there, McDonald cut the boar's throat :
easy enough in theory but not so easy to throw
a heavy and savage old boar.   However, often
enough, on account of the rough ground covered
with scrub and wild vines, which took some
forcing through, McDonald could not arrive
in time, for the two fighting dogs could soon
settle the boar without anyone's assistance. Both
of them carried the scars of boar's tusks, mostly
got before they perfected their team-work ;
and once Valour's life had been despaired of,
but he fought death with the same shining courage
that had brought him under the shadow of it,
and it was that, more than the careful nursing,
that had brought him around.

Such were Valour and Courage who lived
up to their names and were afraid of nothing
in the world or under it ; but to return to Jack ;
on this occasion he was with Mrs. Dobson, who
was pushing her infant child in a pram along

a right of way through the Park. Jack was hunting away in the bracken beside the path. Every now and then he brought a rabbit which he had taken and Mrs. Dobson slipped it into the pram under the child's blanket. Young McDonald was tickled to death and he took care not to show himself and embarrass Mrs. Dobson. He was very struck by Jack's smartness, and, as the son of a neighbouring squire had a lurcher of which he was inordinately proud, he conceived the plan of matching Jack against him ; he later went and saw Dobson and asked him if he would lend him Jack some afternoon ; Dobson readily agreed but said that he would have to come as well, or else once McDonald had slipped Jack he would be unable to take him up.

McDonald, rather foolishly as it happened, said nothing of the hoped-for match but simply told Dobson that he wanted Jack to catch a rabbit or two ; then he went and saw the owner of the other dog and backed himself to produce a dog to beat his the best out of three rabbits, the kill only to count. An afternoon was agreed upon and in the morning Taylor bolted with ferrets and netted three strong rabbits.

McDonald arranged to meet Dobson at the lodge gates of the Park, and they walked together to an open space where the coursing was to take place. Dobson, who knew very well from experience where the rabbits lay, told the other that he was afraid that they would find no rabbits thereabouts, and he was then told for the first time that the rabbits were to be dropped. He said nothing but when they came up to the others, and there was quite a small crowd collected to see the match, he went quietly up to a friend of his and told him to back the other dog to beat Jack for all that he could get on.

One of the rabbits was loosed and when he had gone some way the signal given for the dogs to be slipped, the other dog went on and caught it without any very great difficulty but still in not very convincing style. Jack simply watched the course but made no attempt to join in. Jack would never course a dropped rabbit, for he was wise enough to see no sense in fashing himself for what had been already his.

There was nothing for McDonald to do but to pay up and look cheerful, but the wily Dobson was not done with yet by a long way. He whispered to McDonald to make another match on wild rabbits. McDonald was not too keen, but Dobson insisted that Jack could not be beaten and the other dog's owner was only too keen to make the match on the same terms, double or quits ; and Dobson told his friend to back Jack to win this time. Odds were freely laid against Jack, but as soon as they got to the part of the Park where the rabbits lay and one was put up, Jack nailed it in a flash without giving his opponent a look in, and retrieved it to his master's hand. A minute later Dobson's sharp eye spotted a rabbit in her seat ; he walked over and kicked it up and Jack, who though led by McDonald had always kept one eye on his master, had taken it almost before the other dog knew that one was afoot. Thus the two chief parties to the matches came out all square, but Dobson won on both of them besides getting a present for the loan of his dog ; however, Dobson was not one that often came out second.

Mrs. Dobson was a worthy wife to him. Once he was seen by two beck-watchers to carry home a ten or fifteen-pound poached salmon. The watchers followed him closely into his cottage, confident of success. As they went into the cottage they passed Mrs. Dobson coming out carrying her baby. They searched the cottage high and low without success, Dobson the while standing by watching ; although they found no salmon they found the clue to the mystery, for they found Dobson's baby, but they were too busy looking for the salmon to think of him and never thought that the baby that Mrs. Dobson had carried out was indeed the searched-for salmon.

Dobson confined himself almost entirely to taking wild game, but he once lifted a goose from a nearby farmer, Burton, whom he disliked. The late owner of the goose suspected Dobson, and he got into his pony trap, picked up the village policeman, and drove over to search Dobson's place. They found Mrs. Dobson plucking the stolen goose on the kitchen table : Burton identified it but Dobson maintained that he had got it from his brother ; and to settle the matter Burton and the policeman drove off to question the brother. Dobson knew well enough that his brother would back him up if he could, but as he did not know the circumstances it would be easy for Burton to trap him into admitting that he had not let George Dobson have any goose.

Dobson's brother lived almost two miles away, but by road it was farther, as the road had to follow the valley. Dobson set off across the fells to race the trap ; great runner though he was he was taking something on, for the going was very rough and Burton was justly proud of his trotting pony, and, at last feeling sure that they had Dobson caught, they wasted no time. Dobson had scarcely got to his brother's farm, located him in the byre, and told him the facts, before Burton drove up. Dobson slipped up into a loft and listened to his brother telling the discomfited Burton that he had only the day before sold his brother George a fine grey goose. However just his cause there was nothing more to be done and Burton had to let the matter drop.

Dobson came quite often to Wancheate Farm, for he was very fond of wild-fowling on Lake Southermere, which was often cold work, and he liked to return to the farm to warm his frozen body inside and out. But perhaps the most frequent visitor was Lady Ursula Stuart. She was then something over twenty and had recently come from Scotland after marrying the squire. She could scarcely be described as pretty and was

far from smart, for she took no trouble about her
appearance, but there was about her a kind of
gay and careless splendour that was most attractive.
She came often to Wancheate, for she liked
the wild grandeur of that corner of the country ;
the fishing in the Scarsdale Beck was some of
the best on the estate, and she liked to watch the
eagles soaring over the crags overlooking the lake.
She was fond also of John Todhunter and she
felt rather sorry for him in his voluntary loneliness.   Most of all, Ursula was very interested
in sheepdogs.   She knew that Todhunter had the
best dogs in the district, and that he was probably
the best handler alive.   She liked to go with
him when he was shepherding and see his dogs
work.

With Ursula, Todhunter's usual dour nature
thawed somewhat, for she was a sort of female
Peter Pan, a very child in spite of her twenty-
odd years and her baby girl at the Manor, and
it was impossible for anyone to be surly with
her for long.   Ursula was the only human being
besides Todhunter whom Beth got to know at
all well, for often in her presence Todhunter
took Beth out and schooled and worked her, and
with Ursula Beth got a little out of the habit

of slipping away in the presence of strangers. Ursula did little to cure Beth of her shyness, it was simply that Beth made something of an exception in her case and tolerated her.

CHAPTER VI

BETH'S EDUCATION

As the summer progressed Todhunter slowly and gradually got his two pups to working on sheep. The shepherding in the hot weather consisted mostly in keeping the sheep clear from wicks, as the hill men call the maggots, and this was no light work. A sheep badly wick'd in hot weather would be dead in two days, and it was Todhunter's practice to look over his flocks on alternate days. The higher-fell flock one day and the lower flock on the next.

The work was hard on the dogs and he set out very early each morning to get as much done as possible before the heat of the day. Early work was better, not only for the dogs but for the sheep as well; for in the heat the sheep, and especially those struck, lay about under stones, in the scrapes that they had made, or in any shady spot they

could find and often would not move for any
dog ; besides, in such places they were very
easily overlooked.

Todhunter gathered up the sheep with the
dogs, and, while the dogs held them up, caught
any sheep that were dirty, cut away the dirt
where the flies might strike, and treated
any that were already struck. The pups
were useful there for they could get around the
mob of sheep and help Meg and Fly to keep
them together till Todhunter could see the
dirty sheep and get his crook, a ewe's horn
fitted on to a three-foot hazel, under the sheep's
throat and catch it.

The pups soon learnt to get around the sheep
and soon to go out a little way and gather a few
and bring them up to their master, who gradually
got them on to the stop, come in, fetch on, and
go out whistles. The stop whistle was a single
note "whiew" as high as it could be made,
and indeed that is the almost universal stop
whistle, because dogs stop better for a really
shrill note than for any other. "Come in"
was rather like a curlew's call "whor-whe,
whor-whe" and "fetch on," or "drive on"
though, of course, it was long before they learnt

to do the latter, three notes, "whe-whu-who" and "Go out" "whew-who-o-o," the long hollow "who-o-o" being really the go out note, for an old dog would go out left or right according as he substituted the left or right whistle for the "whew" before the "who-o-o." The left whistle was "whit-whit" and the right "whe-whew," but it was some time before he started to teach the two last.

Todhunter's method of getting pups on to his whistles was to encourage them by signs and voice to do what he wanted and, when they did so, to give the corresponding whistle while they were doing it ; till by and by they associated each whistle with its movement, and at last would work for the whistle alone. This method might be slower than some others but Todhunter preferred it as it developed the pup's inherited instincts ; while he thought pups taught in other ways, though as easy or easier to move, worked in an artificial manner ; they moved about on their sheep entirely as they were bidden and seemed to have no initiative of their own. Only the dog knows exactly the right spot to command his sheep and the man cannot put him there ; besides, Todhunter's dogs often had to work entirely out

of his sight and he could always rely upon them
to carry out their job without his having to be
continually whistling at them. His dogs got
so that they would often even anticipate his
orders ; when, for instance, he opened a gate
into a field where sheep were, one of his old bitches
would stand looking up at him, and, on the
slightest sign giving her permission to run, she
would dash away, gather the sheep and fetch
them through the gate.

Beth and Jess did not come on at exactly the
same rate, nor even one always faster than the
other, for Beth more readily got around sheep
and held them up, but Jess earlier went out
and gathered sheep at a distance in good style.
Beth was keen enough to go after them, indeed
she was too keen and straight-necked. She
went too close to them on her outrun instead
of taking a wide sweep and getting well beyond
them. Todhunter knew that she was inclined
to be shy and he was afraid to stop her too often
for fear that she would give up, but as she got
confidence on her sheep he was the better able
to stop and gently correct her when she went
too near on her outrun. She presently began
to get better, and, though it was not done in

a day, in time she had a wide enough outrun to please anyone.

Once around her sheep Beth readily pulled them towards her master, and the difficulty that he had to contend with was that she was too keen and inclined to hurry them. If a stubborn sheep stopped and faced her, she would stand up to it and if it would not move pretty soon she was liable to go in and bite the sheep in the face ; biting in the face might be permissible in extreme cases but it would not do to make a habit of it, and Todhunter did not encourage a green pup in it, but stopped her rather when she became too eager.

Todhunter's real difficulty began when he started to move Beth from behind her sheep ; she was hot and strong-eyed, perhaps almost over-eyed, and her nature made her most reluctant to leave that position where she felt that she had command over her sheep. Todhunter persevered and kept at her but it was uphill work and Jess came on ever so much faster. Only once Todhunter half got out of temper and tried rating to shift Beth out from behind her sheep : she came, but rather sulkily, and as an old ewe tried to break away, Beth raced back, not with

the usual grand wide turn that she then had,
but straight in, and met the ewe in the face, her
teeth flashed and she cut the ewe's face deeply.
Then, as the frightened ewe nipped back to
the others, Beth dropped and looked defiantly
up at Todhunter. It was useless to rate her
for biting, for it was the rating that had made
her bite : Todhunter called her in a little
sharply :

" That'll do, Beth, come in to me, that'll
do."

Beth got up and came in, half-sulkily, half-
brazenly, like a small boy that knows he has
earned a beating and means to carry it off, but
Todhunter did not beat her, he put her on a
string, a thing she very rarely wore, and then
sent Fly out to gather the sheep. He made
Beth lie down and with Meg's assistance caught
the bitten ewe : it had a deepish flesh wound
in the cheek but it was bleeding freely and would
probably be all right so Todhunter let it go. He
picked up the end of Beth's string and walked
off. While he led her he paid no attention to
her but let her think over the wrongdoing by
herself, which on a string she would do. Before
he got home, however, he let her off and then

sent her out to fetch some sheep to him ; she did it all right, and, without attempting to move her from behind them, he called her off and went home. After that he was very careful how he rated Beth.

Although Beth was slow in coming, Todhunter realised that if she was not spoilt she had in her the makings of the wisest and best sheepdog that he had ever seen. There was no mistaking her wisdom, she showed it continually, and she showed as clearly the marks of high class : she would lie watching the sheep flat on the ground, even her chin on the ground, only her big prick ears up ; and then as the sheep moved, scarcely waiting for the order, she would be going in a flash at racing pace, to drop as quickly, as she got into her position of command. She usually lay with one foreleg stretched out before her and the other bent under her at the knee and her quarters drawn under her, but whether the foreleg was bent for speed in getting up or going down or both, both movements were too quick to see. She could stop so suddenly that on loose ground there were sometimes little spurts of earth or gravel from under her feet. For all her speed there was nothing jumpy about her :

she moved with a swift, smooth rush like deep mountain water, and could be as slow and careful as a stalking cat.

Todhunter, therefore, took infinite pains with Beth, a good deal more than he took with Jess, who, though she would almost certainly be a good useful bitch, could never come up to the class that Beth might reach. But, though he took more trouble and time with her, Todhunter was too wise to pay more attention to Beth, for he knew that that would do her no good but harm and make her stupid and conceited.

As the weather got cooler in the autumn Todhunter had more time to spare from his sheep, and as he had saved his scant crop of hay he went oftener, when the wind was right, in search of venison on the top of Hellaw. Fly was getting old and slow and Meg was gun-shy, indeed she was afraid of thunder and would not work if there was any about. So Todhunter, who had come to love the very sight of Beth, thought to teach her the business that she might take her mother's place. The first few days that she was out Todhunter put Beth on a string towards the finish of any stalks ; and Beth had pretty well learnt the business by the time that she had seen a couple shot : she learnt from Fly's example, and as the stalks were all upwind she could smell the deer and that helped her to learn what they were after.

Then one day Todhunter wounded a brocket. The brocket went off with the others apparently not much the worse, but Todhunter lay down and waited till he saw his deer fall out from the others and go slowly on out of sight ; then he whistled up Fly and Beth, whom he had made lie down when he started on the last and most difficult part of his stalk. He put Beth on a string and walked on till he crossed the line of the brocket after he had fallen out from the rest. To follow the blood scent was no great test of a nose, and Fly, as soon as given permission, went away, with Todhunter and Beth still in a string following as fast as they could. Todhunter dared not let Beth go, for she was a great deal faster than the old and halt Fly and might go on on her own, come up to the deer, go in too rashly, and perhaps be killed.

Fly, and afterwards Beth, failed as deerhounds in that they were silent at the bay ; this made it more difficult to find them, but on the whole it suited Todhunter, as it was less likely that a passing forester might also find the bay. Tod-hunter knew the country as well as his own house and he expected to find his deer at bay in the Ravensdale Beck. He presently came over a brow to see the brocket up over his hocks in a pool with Fly lying panting on the bank : it looked a good place where an accident was not likely to occur so he let Beth go. She saw the deer and Fly and raced away down the steep slope to the beck as keen as mustard.

As Beth came up her keenness affected Fly and the two of them went in straight and hard one at each side. The brocket had only knobblers and little brow antlers and he was unable to do very much damage or use his feet with any great effect in the deep water, but Todhunter, who had intended to slip quietly up and get another shot, was afraid for his two bitches, and he raced down the fellside at his best pace hoping to break the bay, for if they had to run a bit farther and tire themselves the dogs might keep off a bit till he could get up. The brocket, however, was hard hit, his wound was taking effect and he was flustered by the dogs, so he would not leave his pool even when Todhunter came right up.

There seemed little chance of a shot without risk to Beth or Fly, for they were sometimes in the water, sometimes on land, and sometimes even clinging to the deer's head and ears.

Todhunter got excited, dropped his rifle, drew his knife, and went into the mêlée ; and a battle royal then ensued. Fly and Beth, encouraged by Todhunter's presence, redoubled their efforts and, in fact, rather got in his way than otherwise, the brocket plunged and fought this way and that, and raked sideways with his small antlers, and matters were made still more difficult by the spray from the beaten water which flew in all directions. Finally Todhunter got a hold of an antler with one hand and used his knife with the other.

Fly, who was old and experienced, had escaped any injury ; Todhunter had got no more than a cut hand, torn clothes, and a thorough wetting, but Beth was a bit knocked about and had a long clean cut along her ribs, still it was not deep and she was at least well entered to deer ; and the cut might, though this last was doubtful, teach her some caution in future.

Todhunter continued to take Beth with him whenever he went deer-poaching, though often she was not needed and, indeed, often he never got a shot at all. Beth soon learnt that, when out after deer, Todhunter wished to avoid meeting anyone, and that he took notice always whether there was anyone about before crossing a brow into the next dale. Indeed from her own natural dislike to strangers she probably learnt this sooner than do most poaching dogs, and all poaching dogs worthy of the name learn it sooner or later. When out deerstalking as Todhunter had always, as long as he was looking for deer, to walk upwind, Beth was often able to wind Bellis or Patterson if they were before them, before Todhunter could see them ; she would growl quietly and Todhunter would clear off as quickly as he could, for he was no Dobson and had no trust in his legs to carry him out of a scrape if he was seen.

Todhunter did not believe that meat was a suitable diet for sheepdogs and very rarely gave any, but he wanted Beth to run savage at deer, and he always gave her the liver at the gralloch : she soon became keen enough to please anyone and her work at deer made her rather rougher than she might otherwise have been on sheep, and less tolerant of a stubborn sheep. Todhunter hated above all things a dog to give back when working on sheep so he never rated Beth for roughness when he thought that there was any excuse for it, and Beth was too good a sheepdog to be rough for roughness' sake.

CHAPTER VII

MOORE'S HAWKS

ONE day in the late summer, Todhunter, for a wonder, got some lawful venison : one of his lambs was crag-fast high up in the Black Crags, it had got into a spot which looked most suitable for a falcon's eyrie and seemed unapproachable from above or below ; the wonder was how it had got in at all and Todhunter was sure that it could not get out by itself without a broken neck and he went to ask Moore to come with a rope and get it out. It was nothing very extraordinary for sheep to get crag-fast at Wancheate and usually came about by their continually hopping down after a bit of green, till they chanced to drop over a jutting ledge which would not allow them to jump up again. When a sheep was crag-fast in an awkward spot Todhunter always got Moore to get it out, for he was used to taking the young falcons from their nests and was at home on a rope. The ewe was trying to get in to her lamb from above and Todhunter, afraid that she might get stuck too, sent Beth up to shift her down to the bottom where she could not get into trouble.

It was in the evening when Todhunter went to ask Moore to come out some time in the next day or two, for he was in no great hurry, as the lamb would be the better for hungering a little and would be less likely to jump off its narrow ledge when Moore got down to it. Moore was sitting on a chair before his door with a falcon on his fist. She was a falcon of two or three moults and had her complete adult plumage, and lovely she looked with her dark slate back and almost black head and cheeks, and her black-barred salmon breast. She had but lately been drawn from the mew after the moult, and Moore was getting her in flying order ready for the grouse. She sat barefaced on his hand pulling at the stump of a pigeon's wing. She was wild as yet and stopped every now and then to stare anxiously about her. After satisfying herself that all was quiet she went on with her pulling, tearing the quills out by the roots and snapping the small bones as though they had been match-stalks. She ate hungrily, for she had just been enseamed, physicked and made to swallow small pebbles to clear from her inside the fat accumulated during her long idleness in the mew.

As Todhunter came up Moore quietly slipped the hood on to his falcon.

" Shall I be in t'road, Joe ? " Todhunter asked. " I'll stop here by t'yatt an I'll flate her."

" Nay, John, she'll be first rate, she's just a lile bit ower wild for noo," he slipped the hood off once more and the falcon promptly bated violently from the fist, hanging head downwards by the jesses on her legs and frantically beating her wings.   Moore gently pushed her up with his right hand, and, as she regained her footing and stared wildly about her evidently contemplating bating once more, he took a piece of tender lean beef out of his pocket and as soon as she started to pull confidently at that he slipped it away and kept her working at the tough wing.

All the while Moore kept looking anxiously about him, and presently he saw a tiny black dot very high in the sky. The falcon had her back turned and was busy feeding so she did not notice anything and Moore hooded her up without further excitement. The dot in the sky approached rapidly and was followed by two more, soon they could be seen to be hawks and their bells could be heard, heavy hack bells to prevent them as far as possible preying for themselves. Soon they were over Moore's cottage and in a minute were joined by two more, and then another. All six of them started to play amongst themselves, soaring, wheeling, and tilting in the wind, stooping at each other, throwing up, and carrying out every imaginable aerial manœuvre.

These were Moore's hack hawks, six young peregrines, four falcons and two tiercels, that had recently been taken from their nests and were now flying at liberty to develop their strength and adroitness on the wing : as yet they had never preyed for themselves and until they learnt to do so they would return night and morning to be fed, or rather they would not leave in the morning till they had been fed. The heavy hack bells would prevent them preying for a while, but as soon as they began to do so and showed it by their absence at meal-times, Moore would snare the delinquents at the next meal that they attended and begin their training. As long as they attended regularly for meals they would be given about a month at hack.

All six were in the immature brown plumage but one falcon and the two tiercels were a good deal darker than the others. Moore pointed them out saying :

" Yon's t'beggars te catch t'groose, yon dark 'uns from Wolf Crags beyant Borodale. I ne'er had owt from yon crags but were gay good 'uns, this yane's from there," pointing to the falcon yet on his fist. " I ne'er get tercels save from there, tercels canna' hodd a groose often, but yon lile beggars'll hodd owt." Then pulling from his waistcoat pocket an enormous silver watch, whose ticking could be heard for yards, he said: " I maun feed t'lile beggars noo." He got up and went into his cottage taking the falcon with him.

Four of the young hawks had taken stand, three on the roof of the cottage, and one in a nearby elm tree ; while the other two, tired of their sport, were soaring at an immense height to cool themselves in the upper air. After a moment Moore came out with six lures slung over his shoulder, each weighted with lead to prevent the hawks carrying it away and with the evening meal firmly tied to it. As Moore came out he blew through his lips making a " Br-r-r-r " sound which carried well. In a moment the four hawks, who had been sitting down, were in the air. Moore threw out a lure to each, each lure some little distance from the next. The hawks were soon on them and after a little squabbling took separate lures : one falcon tried unsuccessfully to carry hers off in her feet.

One of the two soaring hawks then came down and was almost immediately followed by the other. The first one half-closed her wings as though to stoop, but instead of stooping vertically she came in a beautiful spiral dive, which she adopted to prevent the frightful speed which a vertical stoop from that height would have soon got up and which would have been an unnecessary strain on her frame when she was not flying wild quarry. The other came in a series of vertical stoops, checking herself every fifty or hundred feet and thus stopped herself getting up too much pace. The last two got their lures and all six fed as though they had never fed before nor expected to do so again, only occasionally breaking off to glance suspiciously at Todhunter and Moore, both of whom kept well back. When they had finished they one by one flew rather sluggishly up on to the cottage roof or into one of the trees to spend the night.

Todhunter was just going on home when Sir Ian Stuart rode up. The old thoroughbred horse he was riding was slouching idly along with his head on the floor and had to be kept going all the while for fear that he would pull up altogether. As soon as Ian allowed him he stopped and started to pick grass. Even his beautiful bright bay coat failed to redeem his slovenly, good-for-nothing appearance, but after he had been grazing for a minute or two he heard one of Stump's foxhounds, bored with his summer idleness, hunting something in the distance. The old horse threw up his head and ears and stood listening eagerly : it was easy then to believe that he had been a brilliant hunter, he was not handsome but there was a keen, brave look about his lean old head that there was no mistaking. No Quarter had had a great reputation in the Midlands before the old squire died and Ian, coming to take his place, had brought the old horse to hack about, for it was impossible to ride to the local fellhounds.

Ian had come to ask Moore to give Bellis a hand with the deerhounds in the morning, for he had people staying at the Manor and was having a field day ; but Moore had to take up a falcon at dawn, who, only just in work, had taken off that afternoon and gorged before Moore could find her so that he had been unable to take her down : he was confident of getting her in the morning, but if he was not there at daylight she might go off and perhaps would not be so easily found again. Todhunter offered his services which were gladly accepted, and, as the wind was more or less in the north and they would have to start operations from the Wancheate end of Hellaw, he further offered to put up the foresters with their dogs for the night. Todhunter then went off home and Ian rode off to send the foresters up to Wancheate Farm before dark.

Presently they arrived, Bellis was leading Geraint, Astur, Lion and Mail, and Patterson held the brilliant Valkyrie's no less brilliant litter, Sword, Spear, and their sister Shield ; their names, though, were the wrong way about for there was nothing of defence about Shield, she was all for attack and almost too hot, but Sword, though by no means backward in attack, had really earned the title shield for he had once saved Ian's life : he had started at a hart alone, for Ian had not really been looking for deer, nor was he in a part where he expected to see any, but had taken Sword as a companion. He came suddenly upon an old solitary hart that he had long coveted but whose cunning had been too much for him. Sword, in fact, was not even on a lead so Ian could not have prevented him going even had he wished. After a short course Sword brought his hart to bay in a pool in a beck. The royal hart was fat and heavy and no great runner, but he was formidable when at bay, and he seemed to realise that that was his best chance, for he refused to break his bay, so Ian went in with the knife to try and finish the matter, but it was not easy with only the one dog to help ; the hart knocked him down and looked like settling him when Sword, disregarding the hart's heavy armoury, sprang smash into his face, and the hart, missing his feet, blundered on to the top of Ian who managed to reach up and use his knife. Ian came out practically unhurt but Sword was not fit for work again that season.

The hart had rather a fine level head with all his rights and three on top on each side, which last made him royal, nothing to do with a " hart royal proclaimed " a term of ancient venery meaning a hart which, after giving the king great sport and beating off his hounds, was proclaimed in all the villages near where he was lost and through which he might pass on his return to his original covert, lest anyone taking advantage of his exhaustion and subsequent stiffness should take or kill him.

One of the best known of these examples of a king's gratitude for sport is in Dorset where there is a village of Kingstagg and a Green Man Inn. There is still there to this day a village sign with a picture of a white hart with a ring about his neck on one side and on the other this legend :

> " *When Julius Cæsar landed here*
> *I was then a little deer.*
> *When Julius Cæsar reigned king*
> *He put around my neck this ring*
> *Whoever me shall overtake*
> *Save my life for Cæsar's sake.*"

The origin of this improbable rhyme is that a king, possibly Henry III., had great sport with the hart, very likely found in the New Forest, and proclaimed him. The " Green Man " shot the hart and was himself hanged for it and his lands heavily fined, hence the inn sign of the green-clad archer.

CHAPTER VIII

DEER-COURSING

IAN was a stickler for getting as much of the work as possible done in the cool of the morning. The dogs were as fit as they could be made but that would not prevent them, after a long course in the heat, from blowing and sweating, the last, of course, only through the mouth, and would make it difficult for them to close their mouths and keep their holds on a powerful hart. Ian, therefore, hounded Ursula out of bed before four o'clock. Ursula, never a good getter-up, was further incensed because Ian, to leave, as he said, more room in the trap, was riding No Quarter and did not need to start so early : so that after seeing the others up he went back to bed.

The chestnut mare, Cherry, was waiting in the trap before the door and they set off best pace towards Wancheate. Cherry was keen and Ursula thought that if she could but reach

Wancheate before No Quarter she would be able to get more than her own back on Ian for his ill-timed humour when she was getting up. The Wancheate track was far from a good road, and was made the more difficult by the half-light of dawn, so that at the pace that they were going there was no chance to dodge the more uneven parts. Cherry needed no whip, but went tearing up the track, often cantering, and trotting as fast as she could even over the roughest parts. The trap bumped over the stones which scattered the path, rocked from side to side, and was more than once in grave danger of precipitating the lot of them into the beck ; but Ursula turned a deaf ear to the protests of the others and kept Cherry going.

When they rounded the end of the Black Crags and came in sight of the farm without a sign of Ian, Ursula flattered herself that she had him beaten, but almost immediately Cherry put up her ears, took a firmer hold of the bit, and went off harder than ever. Ursula could only see the short way back to the turn and hear little above the clatter of the trap, but she guessed that Cherry had heard No Quarter, so she kept a sharp look-out over her shoulder, thereby arousing a fresh storm of protest from her wretched passengers, and the instant that No Quarter appeared around the corner she pulled Cherry into a steady trot, not without difficulty, for Cherry had thoroughly entered into the spirit of the race, and pretended that she had never been hurrying at all.

No Quarter came striding up, pulling hard, a sure sign that he had been well set alight, for he was usually the idlest of goers, sweating, and lathered white where the reins had rubbed his neck. Ursula observed these signs with considerable satisfaction and did not fail to remark upon them, but unfortunately her triumph was somewhat spoilt for Cherry was even hotter.

" It's no good your pretending that you've not been racing, Urs'la," Ian said, " but I'll hand it to you that you're no mean Jehu, and I began to be afraid that you'ld do me, too. We'ld best let them walk now and cool off till we get there."

Once at Wancheate the horses were freed of their tack and turned into a field, and the party with Bellis, Patterson, and Todhunter, and the seven deerhounds were soon climbing up the Wancheate Gill.

Even at the farm the blaring of the crag-fast lamb could be heard and every now and then his mother answered him from the bottom of the cliff. As they neared the cliff Todhunter thought that the lamb had moved and he borrowed Bellis's glass to make more certain ; sure enough, the lamb was some way to the right of, and below where he had been the previous day. Todhunter was greatly surprised, for he had thought it impossible for the lamb to move, and as he would not be needed till a suitable deer had been seen and could travel a great deal faster up the fells than some of the squire's guests who were not used to rough going, he bore off to the right of the track to get a closer look at the spot where the lamb then was. When he got beneath the cliff Todhunter found that the lamb had moved into a much better spot and was, in fact, working its way slowly down from ledge to ledge encouraged by the anxious blaring of the old ewe below. While Todhunter watched the lamb completed the descent, sometimes sliding for a little way on his hocks and quarters but always stopping in time to avoid an accident. As soon as the ewe and lamb had reunited, Todhunter set off after the rest of the stalking party, still wondering how the lamb had got off its original ledge.

On coming out on to the top of the Black Crags the ground was examined, though with little hope of success, and as no deer were to be seen the party went on towards Deep Dale making their way over the shoulder of The Dodd, a great hummocky hill nearly three thousand feet high. Before they reached The Dodd they saw a fine flight at a snipe by a pair of wild merlins. The snipe endeavoured to take the air, but both merlins, of whom the jack was easily distinguishable by his grey plumage and smaller size, almost at once gained the sky of him, and the snipe had to rely entirely on his quickness to avoid the repeated stoops of his pursuers, stoop though is hardly the right word as the merlins did not tower above their quarry and stoop from a height as falcons do, but rather closely followed his turns and buckles, and by darting in attempted to bind to him.

The whole flight closely resembled a course at a hare by a pair of high-class greyhounds, the merlins having the same advantage in speed, while the snipe was the quicker on the turn. The open fell offered no covert other than a few scattered stones and the flight lasted for nearly a mile, the snipe repeatedly throwing out his pursuers and keeping generally about the same height from the ground. Although the actual point of the flight was less than a mile the birds really covered two or three times that distance owing to the repeated turns and twists. Towards the end only those lucky enough to have a glass were able to follow the flight and even they could only see the hawks and snipe when they rose and were silhouetted against the sky. Finally the snipe was seen to dive into a thick patch of sieves and the two hawks stooped at him almost together. As neither hawk was seen to rise from the sieves, Ian concluded that they had probably killed, for the merlin is far less often successful in the air than at the actual moment of entering covert; the quarry dare not enter covert at the desperate speed at which it has been travelling for fear of smashing itself, and the merlin, knowing this, makes a dart at the instant the quarry checks itself to enter the covert, and this final dart is very often successful.

As the party toiled wearily up the shoulder of The Dodd, Ian endeavoured to lighten their task by describing another flight he had seen by a wild merlin at a lark : there was a gale blowing at the time and both merlin and lark, lifted on the wind, mounted almost in a moment to a great height, which could only have been achieved on a calm day by many minutes of hard ringing. The merlin stooped repeatedly at the lark but in the wind was easily thrown out. Each time as the merlin threw up from her stoop, the wind caught her and flung her many yards from her intended quarry : the merlin came up again, the two birds seemed for an instant almost to touch and then like leaves were blown far apart. At last they had gone out of sight, the merlin still resolutely battling with the gale.

As they climbed higher, more country came into view and Ian pointed to a distant heap of stones, called " Charm's Cairn." In a winter some years before a man had gone out with a little terrier bitch, Charm, and had not returned : an extensive search was made but no traces could be found, and he was given up as lost. Three months after the man had disappeared Bellis, whose business took him to one of the wildest parts of the Forest of Hellaw, saw Charm in the bottom of a deep gill, and on investigation found the dead body of her master. The man had evidently fallen down into the gill and had either been killed instantly or been so badly hurt that he could not climb out, in which case he would, of course, very soon have died ; and for three months Charm had kept watch beside the dead body of her master. How she had lived was never absolutely found out, but as she was not more than a mile or two across the fells from Todhunter's sheep, she would most likely have always been able to find some dead sheep which were fairly common in the winter, and she had probably made daily excursions for food to some carcase or other. Ian had caused a cairn to be made to the honour of Charm's great loyalty.

By the time Charm's story had been told the party had skirted Brown Dale and were coming over the shoulder into Deep Dale. Deep Dale was an almost sure find at that time of the year and strict silence was the order. And it was as well that it was, for Shield, who had been pulling in the couples steadily throughout, suddenly stopped dead, blew violently through her nose, and stood for a moment head and ears up, snuffling loudly ; the next instant and she leapt into her collar with such force as almost to pull Patterson over. All the other dogs were immediately affected by her excitement, some stood staring about with heads up and sniffing, endeavouring to get a view or the wind of the deer which they believed Shield to have located, while others either themselves winding the deer, or putting complete trust in Shield's nose, or else in the hope of getting a nearer look, pulled madly at their leads.

Such was Shield's excitement that she began to cry softly and Ian, adjuring Patterson to keep " that little devil Shield " quiet at all costs, proceeded quietly forward alone to try and get a look at the deer. The ground was a round shoulder and so his horizon was very limited and he could do nothing but continue carefully straight forward and trust to seeing the deer before they saw him. After a little he came to a bit of a rise whence he could see some distance, and approaching this rise with the utmost caution he found himself within a hundred yards of the nearest hind. The little herd consisted of six hinds and two harts and the latter were lying a little by themselves below their wives. The deer could scarcely have been better placed ; by coming at them a little from below they would be forced up the hill and the harts would probably never fairly overtake the hinds so there would be no chance of either of the dogs picking on a hind. Besides this the slope at that end of Deep Dale was comparatively gentle and far more favourable to the dogs than the steeper ground at the head of the Dale.

When Ian rejoined the party he found that Patterson had Shield's head under his coat in his efforts to keep her quiet, and this decided him to take her for one, not because Ursula maintained the chance was hers by right as the first finder of the deer, but because if she was not taken she would pull so hard for the rest of the morning and quite possibly make sufficient noise to frighten the deer. Shield was, therefore, put into slips as was Geraint, who was as sensible as she was hot, and so was less likely than any of the others to be affected by her excitement. As soon as Shield was in the slips and her collar had been taken off she ceased her crying and contented herself with a steady straining pull.

Todhunter and Patterson remained where they were with the rest of the dogs : Bellis turned and climbed up towards the top of The Dodd that he might be in a position to follow the course if they should go that way, but he kept

well behind the shoulder till he should hear the
holla which Ian promised to give on slipping
Shield and Geraint.   Ian went a little way down
the hill and then turned up towards the deer, while
the rest of the party followed some twenty
yards behind him. Presently Ian caught a
glimpse of the topmost hind and he bent double
and then continued on his knees : it was useless
to get lower than his hands and knees as he
was then only a little higher than the heads of
the dogs.   A little farther and he could see the
hind's head once more and the next instant
she had seen him and got to her feet. For
a moment she stood looking at him while the
others also leapt to their feet.   Shield once more
started her whining and even Geraint strained
at the slips : Ian sprang to his feet to see the
nearest hart not sixty yards away : the whole herd
of deer were instantly in full flight diagonally
up the hill going with their peculiar bucketing
action, which though apparently slow, is very
fast, and Ian immediately slipped the deerhounds.

Shield almost at once drew out and was soon
racing up to the harts with a two lengths' lead
of Geraint.   The ground was so favourable to
the greyhounds that they ran up to the harts,

overtaking them nearly one yard in every four :
as Shield drew up the two harts turned slightly
downwards and continued along the side of the
hill, while the hinds turned straight up and were
soon out of sight over the brow. As Shield
drew up the rearmost hart turned downwards
and both dogs followed him, while the other went
on once more up the hill.

The hart then came racing down the hill
with both dogs hard at his heels, for the turn
had let Geraint up, and the three of them presented
the most magnificent sight. Shield once more
drew out and was soon racing level with the hart,
at once she sprang in sideways at his neck, but
she was probably not far enough up, for instead
of seizing the throat she received in mid-air the
full thrust of the hart's shoulder, going as he
was at racing pace. Shield fell heavily and went
skidding along on her side : before she could
regain her feet Geraint leapt over her and a
moment later had sprung in his turn at the
throat, the only hold he was ever known to try
for : he got his hold but the hart carried him
along at almost the same speed as before. By
this time Shield had regained her feet and crossing
behind the hart came up on his other side. She,

too, got her hold and the hart carried both dogs for a little way before he blundered and fell. He made one or two ineffectual efforts to rise but was dead before Ian could come up ; the only wounds he had received were in the throat.

While Bellis remained to attend to the gralloching, the others went on in their search for more deer, but Bellis had long joined them before they saw any suitable deer, although they disturbed two hinds and their calves, who saw them at a great distance and made quickly off in single file, a hind first and last and the two calves in the middle. Presently three deer were seen lying near the top of a steep slope ; on closer examination they were seen to be young deer, probably two brockets and a spire, and as such were not, as they say in Devon, warrantable deer ; and at an ordinary time Ian would not have bothered with them but on this occasion he was anxious to show all possible sport to his party and so was unwilling to lose any chance.

The slope on which the deer were lying was concave so that from their position the deer could see the whole length of it as well as the opposite side of the dale : a direct approach, then, was impossible save straight down off the

top of the slope, and then the stalkers would be
in sight directly they came over the brow ; such
a slip would necessarily be a pretty long one and
quite hopeless, as the deer would naturally go
straight down the hill, which was extremely
steep, and so would further increase their lead so
much that the dogs would have no possible chance
of success, and this more especially as the young
light deer would be faster and much longer-winded
than old and heavy harts. The only hope was
to get the deer up over the brow on to the long
level and fairly wide bank on top, on that ground,
which was very favourable, the dogs would run
up very quickly and might get on terms before
the deer turned down on either side.

After some consultation Ian took Astur and
Mail and with the rest of the party made his way
around to the top of the fell above the deer,
Bellis went around to the opposite side of the dale
and Todhunter and Patterson with the rest of the
deerhounds withdrew to a spot where they would
not disturb the deer nor give the dogs a view
of the course and so excite them. Ian and
the others got into one of the peat holes two or
three feet deep, which abounded on the top of the
bank, at a point a little downwind of the spot

where the deer were, and as nearly as possible where he thought that they would come out over the brow. Bellis then showed himself and by luck or good management, though probably largely the latter, for he had a life's experience of the movements of deer under different circumstances, he was in such a position that the deer came out over the brow within thirty yards of Ian's place of concealment. Ian waited until the deer, which were trotting, had got well away from the brow of the slope and then slipped the deerhounds at rather under a hundred yards.

The slip was not a particularly good one but might be successful with the two dogs that he had and which were much the fastest in the team. Mail, rather the faster of the two, was in his second season and was no great favourite with his master who considered that he lacked courage, he was not afraid of the deer, but was a soft runner, he had an enormous stride and probably largely on that account he would not extend himself on steep or rough ground ; on good ground he was brilliant, but when things were not going just his way he was liable to stop and give up. Astur was also very fast but rather a short runner.

As soon as Ian and the dogs came out of their hole the deer broke into a gallop going straight up the bank and the dogs were immediately slipped : they ran up on the deer very quickly, Mail slightly in front, and the difference between their style of running and that of English greyhounds was very clearly to be seen : they may have carried their heads a little bit higher but the real difference was in their action, for though they had much longer strides they had not the same quickness of recovery and so their action was more level and lacked that undulating motion which is so characteristic of the English greyhound.

The deer finding themselves overtaken made for the slope up which they had originally come ; before they reached it Mail struck once at the quarters of the nearest, but was unable to get a hold, and the next momer' *∵ ∘* three deer were over the brow and racing down the slope, although the slope was so steep that a man walking up it would often use his hands to help him, the deer went straight down it at full gallop and immediately left the dogs far behind. Mail gave up almost at once, but Astur followed them down as best he could, often stumbling and his tail whirling round and round the whole time in

his efforts to keep his balance. The deer, however, in spite of their incredible speed, nearly
twice that of Astur, never once faltered and went
on up the opposite slope and out of sight with
Astur, a long way behind and very blown,
resolutely following. Before long, however, he
returned completely done, having lost them,
and was once more coupled up with Mail who
had never gone down the hill at all.

Some of the party were now of the opinion
that it was no very difficult thing to approach
a deer, but they were soon to be disillusioned
for the party, after descending into the next dale
and coming round a spur into the bottom of the
dale beyond, saw a single hart that had evidently
been disturbed making his way slowly along
near the top of the far hill, he was not in the
least frightened, but was well on the look-out
and for the moment was quite unapproachable.
If he continued his present course, however, he
would soon have to cross a deep gill and while he
was in this gill he would be unable to see the fellside beyond. The gill was the only chance, but
if advantage was to be taken of it no time was to
be lost. Patterson and Todhunter with the
unwanted five deerhounds turned back behind

the spur, but the others with Sword and Spear got into the bed of the beck which flowed down the dale and went up it as quickly as possible. Ian led the way with Bellis, and Ursula brought up the rear and made sure that all kept bent double and out of the hart's sight. Ian and Bellis were soon far in front and when they reached the point where they must climb they saw that the hart had disappeared and was, no doubt, in the gill. Ian at once turned up the fellside and went up as quickly as he could. The ascent was very steep and made the more difficult by the dogs which continually got in his way. By the time he reached the level where he believed the hart to be, he felt as though his lungs would burst, but as yet there was no sign of the deer.

Ian considered for a moment waiting where he was and so meeting the hart in the face as he came out of the gill, but decided not to, as he was not sure exactly whether he was the right level or not. He looked down for the others but saw nothing of them and guessed that they had been too blown to run up the fellside. He advanced cautiously, hoping to get a view of the hart's horns before the rest of him came into sight, and so give himself time to get quite opposite to the hart. More and more of the gill came into view without a sign of the deer and Ian felt that he must be close under his side ; at last he could see the whole of the gill.

The hart was not in the gill, he had gone as though he had never been, although how he had managed to get unseen out of the dale it was difficult to imagine.

The rest of the party, still blowing, toiled up the fellside and paid but little attention to the anecdote which Ursula told on the way up to lighten their climb. She pointed out a small beck which ran into the one they had come up.

" Ian and I call that the ' Tidal Beck.' Once we were lost here on the fells in a mist ; we could see the mist blowing up as we were stalking some deer, but we managed to get a slip before it came ; there was a longish course and, while we were following, the mist came down and we lost the dogs, after a while we got hold of one of them but the other, old Bran, came home at dark. By that time Ian and I were lost, but Bellis said he knew where he was and led the way.

" Bellis is an excellent fellow but he has a conceit that he can't be lost on the fells, although it is easy enough in a mist for a man who has lived on them all his life to get lost. There was no wind to help us and we soon began to suspect that Bellis was lost, too, although he would not admit it. At last we came to that beck. I knew if we followed the water down we should be bound to come down out of the mist and although it might be the wrong way it was better than helpless wandering. Bellis, however, would not hear of it and I felt sure that it was simply because if it brought us out the wrong side it would prove that he had been lost ; so I asked him where it would bring us out, and he said :

" 'Nay, milady, thou maun pay ne heed te yon lile gutter, it whiles runs one way and whiles another.' "

The party, having reunited, had a fruitless search for the better part of two hours before they discovered a herd of deer about half-way up the hill on the opposite side of a dale. Although the deer were not more than three-quarters of a mile away it would be necessary to make a detour of at least two miles before the stalkers could come at them. The herd consisted of a master hart, two or three small male deer and hinds. One of the guests, on seeing that there were three calves in the herd, thought that it would be difficult to keep the dogs from killing them, but Ian explained that though there was but one yeld deer with the three hinds and calves, yet the hinds and calves would manage to throw the onus of the chase upon that single deer.

After a long and difficult stalk, which entailed scrambling up the course of a steep and stony beck and crawling on hands and knees up a shallow gill, they arrived as near to the deer as they could take the dogs without being seen. Ian then got to his feet and, as the whole herd set off along the fellside, slipped Sword and Spear. The slip was a long one and the dogs only gained very slowly on the deer, who appeared able to travel along the steep hillside as well as though they were on level ground, while the dogs were greatly handicapped : at first on leaving the slips there was a good deal of bumping, and even after they had got themselves separated, they were never galloping smoothly on the steep ground. Sword even fell heavily more than once and Spear several times only recovered his balance as though by a miracle. The deer soon disappeared over the shoulder of the hill and the hart was last throughout, not from any chivalrous idea of taking the post of danger but because he was too fat to keep up. The next moment the dogs also were out of sight.

The party followed as fast as they could and strung well out : first Ian running, and slipping and stumbling every few paces, Ursula a moderate second, who, also attempting to run, was making little better time than Bellis, who though no runner could walk at a terrific pace over any ground. The guests "also ran," they were quite deserted by their host and hostess who had completely forgotten them, and by Bellis who despised anyone unaccustomed to the hill, so they followed along as best they could under their own steam, and heavy weather they made of it.

On reaching the brow where he had last seen the course, Ian saw the hart some way off descending the hill at a great pace with Sword and Spear right on him making repeated and unsuccessful attempts to seize and stop him : of the rest of the small herd there was no sign. Once at the bottom of the hill the hart turned down the dale away from Ian, and though both dogs seemed to be all over him it was impossible at that distance to see exactly what was happening, but the hart managed to keep his feet and went out of sight around a spur of the fell. Ian started down the fellside after them : at the point where he had last seen the course the little beck joined the beck from the adjoining dale and became quite a respectable size, and a little way down this larger beck Ian came upon the hart at bay. The hart was obviously very distressed and had several cuts about his neck and thighs where the dogs had endeavoured to get a hold, but the dogs were nearly as tired and Sword was a good deal cut about and had probably rashly tried conclusions with the hart at bay. The bay was in a pool below a rock some ten feet high over which the water fell in a foaming cascade, the right side of the pool also was protected by high rocks overgrown with rowan trees, but the left and lower sides were open.

The hart bayed by the two magnificent deer-hounds was a fine sight indeed and the setting was worthy of it, for besides the beauty of the pool and cascade, the whole dale was particularly grand and wild.

As Ian came up the hart at once broke away downstream. Sword and Spear immediately sprang in at his throat, he missed his feet in the rough beck-bottom and fell. The hart was not born that could get up once Sword and Spear had him down, and Ian quickly finished the matter with the knife. Spear was quite unhurt, but Sword was rather badly cut for he had something of his sister's rashness.

Ian decided that Sword ought to be taken off at once and he sent Bellis with him to the Manor Farm, which was the nearest house, there to have his wounds washed and await the cart which Patterson was to send out for him from the Manor. There was little chance of further sport but Ian took old Lion, and Geraint again, and set off with his party to return to the Manor by way of Mossdale on the offchance of another slip, while Todhunter returned the four remaining deerhounds to the lodge where Bellis lived. Todhunter then went home and received on the next day a haunch of venison in token of his help.

In the evening Ian drove out to Wancheate with two grooms, one of whom drove Cherry back, while he rode No Quarter.

CHAPTER IX

THE WHITE FALCON

THAT winter about Christmas the wild fowl came down on to Lake Southermere in unprecedented numbers, and often at night Todhunter would hear " the hounds of God," flocks of wild geese sounding exactly like a pack of foxhounds passing high overhead. Always the wild fowl moved southwards ever southwards, and all the hillmen said there must be bad weather in the north. Yet the wind blew not out of the north but was for ever changing and came in gusts from every point of the compass.

The last week in January Todhunter felt the pains coming on in his back and a day or two later in the evening he saw a flock of wild swans flying southward, or more correctly a herd of swans, for as the Boke of St. Albans tells us " It is correct to speak of a herd of cranes and swannys, but of a gaggle of geese and women." From which it might reasonably be deduced that the author of the Boke of St. Albans was a married man, whereas, in fact, she was the head of a nunnery, but perhaps that office would breed the same opinion of the fair sex. The herd, then, of swans were flying very high and very fast, for few birds fly faster than the wild swan when he is high and well on the wing, his great weight no doubt increasing his pace when he is fairly going.

There were thirteen swans flying in a great irregular V, seven in one arm and five in the other. As they passed high overhead they were a most splendid sight, all snow-white except where the rays of the dying sun tinged their wings and breasts with mauve and rose. The swans worried Todhunter for they only went to confirm the warning already thrown out by the pain in his back that bad weather was most likely hard on the way. He was afraid for his sheep up on the fell, and yet he dared not bring them down to eat up the scanty pasture in his few enclosed fields, for that would all be needed when

he got the ewes down to lamb in the beginning of April.

The actual weather itself showed no signs
of breaking. Todhunter felt poorly after two
or three days of little food and less sleep, and
he decided to wait until the wind should
change, for he felt that nothing very dreadful
could happen until then.

About noon two days after the swans had
passed, Todhunter was out on the lower fell-
breast with Beth, more for working her on sheep
than to do anything to the sheep themselves.
The weather had shown no change, only
the wind seemed more fitful, but the sheep
appeared stubborn and unwilling to move, and
the pain in Todhunter's back had grown
steadily worse.

He heard an old cock grouse calling.

" Br-r-r ; Br-r-r, go back, go back, go back, go
back," then he cut off in the midst of a " Go back,"
and Todhunter glanced up expecting to see
an eagle : instead, a magnificent white falcon
came sailing southwards over the top of the
Black Crags. She was far larger than any
peregrine though built much on the same lines,
and snow-white on her underside except for

the tips of her wings, but, as she tilted to catch
a flaw of the wind, Todhunter saw that her
back and the upper sides of her wings were
flecked with black, giving something the impression of an ermine cloak.

Todhunter thought that here might be a chance
of a grouse for dinner and he sent Beth out
in the direction that he knew the old grouse
was, but the grouse knew better than to get
up and lay close. When Todhunter realised
that Beth was past where he had heard the
grouse calling, he stopped her and whistled
her in. On the return journey by good luck
she blundered almost on to the grouse, who
went off best pace upwind.

The falcon had passed well downwind of
the grouse before he got up and Todhunter,
who knew that they are better downwind and
prefer to hunt that way, hardly thought that
she would even fly the grouse under such dis-
advantageous conditions ; but she came round
and set off in pursuit, and Todhunter, used
to Moore's trained hawks, was amazed at the
ease with which the falcon came up over the
grouse dead in the wind. She got well over
him, turned over, and stooped, a flashing bar

of silver light ; it was a glorious stoop, harder by far than any Todhunter had ever seen. The old grouse had more than once saved himself from a falcon's stoop, and he now tried his most cunning dodge, shifting at the last moment almost straight upwards. The white falcon, though, was no green eyess deprived by man of her natural training ; she seemed to anticipate the grouse's shift and herself twisted slightly to meet it, so that the grouse shifted smash into the stooping falcon. Todhunter clearly heard the blow, and the grouse, stone dead with his back laid open, was hurled to the ground with such force that he actually rebounded off it. The falcon threw up in perfect style and swept down once more on to her quarry.

Todhunter made in, in the hope of frightening the falcon off her grouse, but he was to be disappointed, for although, unused to men, she allowed him to come pretty close, she presently picked the grouse up in her feet and carried it off apparently without an effort. Todhunter had never before seen a Greenland falcon, the real queen of the air, compared to whom the eagle is like a coal barge to a racing yacht.

In the old days before the extensive enclosure of the land ruined falconry, the Greenland falcon was literally beyond price, being used with others of the great northern falcons, slight falcons, and sometimes the soft-feathered Eastern Sacres, for flights at the kite, the Milan Royal, who in spite of his thieving and carrion-eating nature gave such sport that he was dignified with a royal title.

What a sight it must have been, when the hawking party, near Royston or Newmarket, espied the kite soaring like a speck in the sky, yet easily distinguishable by his long wings and forked tail.

Now one of the servants flies the owl, an eagle owl with a fox's brush tied to his feet, carefully trained to fly to the lure. The kite, thinking to rob the day-dazzled owl of some booty, drops from his lofty pitch, only to find, as he comes fairly near to the ground, the falcons unhooded in his face ; perhaps four great ger-falcons, Greenlanders, Icelanders and Norway falcons, for it is doubtful if even a king ever owned four Greenlanders at once, all entered to the kite.

Now the flight begins ; the kite with an

advantage of perhaps two hundred yards in height, it matters little how far away he may be horizontally, takes the air, mounting in wide rings, and the magnificent gerfalcons ring up after him in the grand and stately style that only the haggard falcon knows. Each takes her own course regardless of the others and her quarry, but striving to mount as fast as ever she can, making use of every eddy of the wind which she thinks may help her. So they mount steadily into the sky to an enormous height, even sometimes till they disappear from view in a perfectly clear sky, and all five drifting downwind at such a pace that the party below have to gallop their horses their hardest.

Now the falcons are above the kite, and the Greenlander, Daughter of the Dawn, the pride of the royal mews, stoops from a height of more than a hundred feet above her quarry. The kite turns over on to his side and throws her out but now all four are stooping in turn one after another, stooping and throwing up, stooping and throwing up, and soon as they slowly descend the falconers can hear the whistling of their wings. The kite turns this way and that, twisting, sideslipping and diving, and losing altitude at every shift.

Now an Iceland tiercel hits the kite hard, and the next moment while he is yet unbalanced from the tiercel's blow, Daughter of the Dawn has bound to him. The other three catch hold and the five grand birds fall slowly to the ground on their widespread wings, more than ten miles from where they were hooded off.

The falconers gallop up, King James, than whom no one has ridden harder, amongst them ; each falconer takes his hawk off the kite, giving her a still warm brown chicken as reward instead of the kite's nauseous flesh, and the King orders that the kite, very little the worse, be let loose as soon as the hawks have been fed and hooded up.

But alas ! those days are over and now the Greenland falcon, who comes to these shores in her winter wanderings, owes it entirely to her great powers of flight if she finish up, not on a royal fist, but in a taxidermist's glass case.

Todhunter did not even know that the falcon was a Greenlander, but he realised that the presence of the " snow falcon," as he called her, so far south meant bad weather in the north. He decided that on the morrow he would go up on to the high fell and gather up any sheep that might have wandered away a little, that in the case of snow he might be able to find them the more easily. Presently he set off home to his dinner, before he reached home he fancied that it had grown colder and that the wind had backed more into the north, but it still blew only fitfully and in gusts. He looked once or twice into the north, but the heights of Hellaw shut in his horizon and he could see nothing.

CHAPTER X

THE GREAT STORM

ABOUT two o'clock Todhunter went into his cottage, made up the dying fire, and set an unattractive-looking stew to warm up. While it was yet heating he thought that it had grown darker, and, being anxious about the weather, he went out to have a look. As soon as he rounded the corner of the cottage and could look into the north he stopped appalled, for the sky looked like the end of the world. Above the Black Crags rolled a great cloud scarcely less black in places than the crags themselves, but it was not solid for it eddied and twisted and was all shades from dove-grey to black, and shot through with bronze and purple lights. Todhunter stood for a moment watching, and then a gust of wind, icy-cold that cut like a knife, brought him back to life. He hurried back into the cottage, pulled on his cap, fastened a sack about his shoulders with a nail used as a pin, and taking up his stick he looked for a moment over his four dogs. Then :

" Come on, Beth—Meg."

Old Fly sensed from his manner that something unusual was up, and she tried to slip out of the door with the other two, but Todhunter thrust her back with his leg saying :

" Get in, auld lass ; it's ne good, I canna tak' the'."

Todhunter had not gone a furlong from the farm when the wind came in a shrieking blast, a wall of air that almost forced him backwards, and he bent himself double as he struggled against it.

Then the snow came, a blinding smother that blotted out the world ; and familiar objects near at hand coming suddenly out of the swirls seemed to belong to some other world till one might have thought that one was wandering with Thor in the Giant Land of the Norse legends. Todhunter struggled on up the Wancheate Gill and then up through Crag Gate. The snow was already obliterating the path and he slipped and stumbled over the stones and screes, and often missed his feet and fell.

The ascent was not only frightfully difficult but actually dangerous; Todhunter, however, struggled almost mechanically on.

When at last he came out on to the top of Hellaw the wind, which came for miles with scarcely a check, buffeted him with redoubled force. He tried to avoid the worst of it by keeping on in the gill, but on top the snow had already drifted deeply in the gill, and that made going in the rough bottom quite impracticable. Todhunter climbed out on to the right side and fought his way on straight into the wind. He dared not let the dogs run into the wind for they would have then been almost at once out of earshot and would have soon lost him : so he kept on till he got well upwind of where he thought the sheep would be. The two dogs walked behind him close at his heel, endeavouring to shelter from the worst of the storm.

When Todhunter thought that he was far enough, he turned back and sent Meg out. She went out of sight at once. Todhunter walked slowly downwind whistling and calling at the top of his voice to let Meg know where he was. Presently, as he saw nothing of her, he stood still, and finally thinking that she was most likely stuck with some sheep, who would not willingly move in the blizzard, he sent Beth out to help her. Beth disappeared in the snow, and Todhunter, after waiting for a while longer, went to try and find them. He saw nothing of them and presently after searching for a while he realised that he had no real idea where he was in relation to the spot from which he had loosed the dogs. He cast backwards and forwards across the wind working always into it and calling.

" That'll do, Meg. That'll do, Beth. That'll do, that'll do," and whistling.

Finally he was aware of Meg, but she came suddenly out of the snow and Todhunter had no idea from which direction she had come. It had then long been quite dark but he continued to look and call for Beth till he fell down a bank and found himself in the Wancheate Gill. He decided that Beth must have gone home and he knew that unless he soon started to do likewise he would most likely never reach it. He set off along the gillside but he had to go carefully for he had little idea how far he was from the edge of the Black Crags, and in the blinding snow he could very easily have fallen over.

When he found himself on the edge of the crags, he worked to his right till he got into the gill and then started down the gate. As soon as he got over the edge and a little out of the wind the relief was enormous, but he had scarcely started down when he realised that the descent was impossible. The steep narrow Crag Gate, not easy in daylight, was in the dark only possible for anyone thoroughly well acquainted with it. But then in the dark and filled with shifting snow it was an utter impossibility.

The only way down was to go eastwards along the top of the Black Crags, get down to the Scarsdale Beckside and come along the track from Stonethwaite, a route more than three times as long as that straight down the Wancheate Gill. The thought of going up once more into the raging wind on top was so frightful that Todhunter was strongly tempted to wait awhile where he was in the lee of the Crags, but no one knew better than he that to stop there was certain death, so he climbed out once more and set off along the top to go round.

In the early hours of the morning Todhunter reached home more dead than alive to find no sign of Beth. He had been for nearly twelve hours through the most frightful ordeal, fetched in no sheep but lost the best dog that he had ever owned. He got outside some whisky, and poured some, much to her disgust, down Meg's throat. Then he set to work with numb fingers to relight the dead fire, over which the stew which was to have been his dinner still hung from the chimney hook. As soon as he got a bit warm the thought of Beth made him so restless that he could no longer keep still. He took a lantern, went out to the byre, roused the sleeping kine, who had missed their evening milking, milked, fed and watered them, and went back to his kitchen to wait for daylight.

As soon as it was light Todhunter set out once more to look for Beth, he took no dog with him but went out alone up the Stonethwaite track.

The blizzard still raged with undiminished fury.

Todhunter climbed out on to the top of Hellaw and by keeping the wind always on his right cheek presently came to the Wancheate Gill. He made his way alongside it till he came to a sharp bend which he recognised and so knew where he was. He then cast systematically backwards and forwards, finishing each westward cast on the gill side so as to make sure of his ground ; he never ceased to call and whistle. After perhaps an hour he heard Beth bark. He made his way in her direction calling still and occasionally hearing her bark, but she made no attempt to come to him for her bark was always in the same place. Of a sudden Todhunter blundered on to a huddled mass of sheep, all with their backs to the wind and their heads down. The next moment Beth came up to him.

The afternoon before she had never seen Meg, but soon after she left Todhunter she had found a dozen or more sheep huddled together. She had hounded them almost by sheer force back to where she had believed Todhunter to be. But he had moved downwind and she could no longer hear him. She had become confused in the snow and got farther away from him. The sheep, who were most reluctant to move at all, became harder and harder to shift, and finally had refused to move altogether. Beth, to whom it had never occurred to go away and leave them, had therefore stopped with them until Todhunter should come and help her. Once the night before she had heard him in the distance but it was against her nature to bark, and Todhunter had unwittingly turned and gone farther away and left her to her lonely vigil.

Beth greeted Todhunter with rather an attractive trick she had which can best be described as " laughing." She would flick back her ears, open her jaws, hang out her tongue, slightly narrow her eyes and look up at her master exactly as though she were laughing. She only did this when she was very pleased over something or thought that Todhunter was pleased with her, which came to the same thing.

Todhunter just leaned down and gently pulled one of her ears with :

" 'Llo Beth. Good lass, Beth."

He made her swallow a little whisky which he had brought with him for the purpose, and with what was left he himself celebrated the success of his search. Then he tried to move the sheep, but they absolutely refused to budge and stood like so many lumps of wood. There was nothing for it but to go on home and leave them, and indeed Todhunter was so pleased to have got Beth back, an event which he had feared was most unlikely, that he turned his back on the sheep fairly cheerfully.

That night the snow ceased, and the wind veered so that for a little it thawed, but the wind soon backed once more into the north and there was a hard frost which slightly crusted the surface of the snow. In the morning Todhunter set out to search for his sheep. He took all four dogs, for though it would be hard work for the lame Fly and for Beth after her long exposure, yet the work before them was likely to be too much for the other two alone, and Todhunter spared neither himself nor his dogs when there was urgent work to be done.

The Crag Gate was quite impassable and would be for several weeks, for in the deep narrow gill the snow was drifted in places ten or fifteen feet deep, and it would be long before it would thaw. Todhunter went round by the beckside, climbed up on to Hellaw and began his search for his sheep. It was hard work for both him and the dogs ploughing through the snow, and he often had to make wide detours to avoid the deeper drifts.

When Todhunter let the dogs run he was

careful to keep Beth and Jess close in to him, because for some reason dogs that will never think of gripping a sheep in the ordinary way, will get hold of sheep in deep snow or in water, possibly from the fear of losing them. Todhunter had no cause to suspect either of the two pups, but until he knew for certain that they were all right he did not take any chances. He found the sheep wherever they had been able to find any shelter, sometimes one or two by themselves and sometimes as many as twenty packed together. Many of them were so packed in by the drifted snow that they could not move; when that was the case Todhunter trod out a path for them, going backwards and forwards treading down the snow till a sufficient path was made. When the snow was deep the sheep were often afraid to go into the narrow path between the high snow walls and it was hard work to get one to start down : when one would go the others followed all right " like sheep."

Todhunter walked along the sides of the little gills and everywhere where he thought that the sheep might have got to for shelter from the wind, for it is the nature of sheep in a storm to get into the lee whenever possible, unlike deer, who rarely do so. In this way sheep often get smothered by the snow drifting over them ; and Todhunter, by poking with his stick into those drifts, which he thought might conceal sheep, found several and dug them out. He had found less than half of his higher fell flock when he was compelled to set off home with those that he had. For, as in many places he would have to tread out a path for them, he knew that it would be a long job taking them down off the fell and home by the beckside. The snow clogged terribly on the wretched sheep's wool, forming into great balls as big as a man's head and so handicapping them that Todhunter had repeatedly to go in amongst them and knock the balls of snow off.

It was long after sunset before they reached home, but as it was a clear night the snow lying on the ground, by reflecting the starlight, made the night almost as light as day. Todhunter turned the sheep into one of the fields in front of the farm where they started to dig under the snow for their food. After lighting his fire and putting his supper on to cook he went out to the byre to attend to his cattle.

That night it froze hard again, and the next

day Todhunter went out to get in his flock from the lower fell. The fell below the Black Crags had been somewhat sheltered and he was able to find most of the sheep with less difficulty than on the previous day. The frost had hardened the top of the snow, and the sharp edges, where they broke through, hurt the dogs' feet so that they all four came home in the evening footsore and weary. And, what was worse, the crust on the top of the snow began to make it difficult for the sheep to get enough food even in the enclosed pastures : Todhunter realised that if it did not soon thaw he would have to feed his sheep or run the risk of their starving. He never fed his hoggs in winter as some farmers did, but let them take their chance on the fell with the older sheep, and so he never made more than enough hay for his cattle ; indeed his farm was so poor that he could not have done so had he wished. He therefore had no hay to feed his sheep.

Todhunter went day after day out on to the fell searching for buried sheep. In this work Beth was presently a great help to him, for she learned to mark buried sheep. This is an inherited instinct which no dog can be taught,

and which only a few dogs have.   She could wind
the sheep, and certain it was that wherever she
started to dig, there would buried sheep be. Sometimes the sheep had fallen into a gill on top of each
other and the bottom ones were dead, and sometimes even those that were alive when they
were dug out were so weak that if, as they were
freed, they struggled out of the snow, the sudden
exertion was too much for their hearts and they
died in the very moment of salvation. It was
extraordinary how the sheep lived under the
snow, for often there were no visible ventilation
holes, and the air must have perforated generally
through the snow.   Todhunter owed the recovery
of a few of his sheep to the foxes.   Foxes could
wind the buried sheep and dug down to them,
and they did no harm for they never, as far as
Todhunter knew, attacked a living sheep other
than a young lamb.   It must have been unpleasant
for the imprisoned sheep to watch the foxes
feasting on their dead companions within a
foot or two of them, but if it led to their discovery
by Todhunter and rescue it was cheap at the
price.

At last Todhunter could bear the sight of his
starving sheep no longer, there was no sign

of a thaw and as Lake Southermere was frozen
and he heard that Burton, who farmed on the
southern slopes of Blenthorpe and whose farm
was close to the lakeside, had hay, he went along
the lakeside on the ice to try and buy some.
Burton, who had a little hay to sell, knew that
Todhunter could not possibly get any elsewhere,
or rather that if he got it he could not transport
it by land, so he thought that he could ask what
he liked for the hay. Todhunter knew that Burton
was not one of those that gave anything away,
and in the circumstances expected to pay a
pretty stiff price : but Burton asked nearly
three times the price even that Todhunter had
feared that he might. At the price it would have
paid Todhunter to let his sheep take their chance,
but it was not pleasant to live among starving
animals, and he bought enough hay to keep
them going. He made a light sled and carted
the hay himself over the three miles of ice,
taking many journeys over it.

Three weeks after the fall the thaw came,
and many were the dead sheep that came to
view as the snow melted from around them,
and the eagles, buzzards, ravens and foxes
who had had a leanish time of it made up by

gorging till they could scarcely fly or run. One day, about a month after the beginning of the thaw but when the snow still lay deep where it had drifted, for the snow dies hard on the high fells, Beth marked so certainly that Todhunter, against his own judgment, began to dig away the snow with his hands. At last he came down on an old ewe still alive but in a terrible way.

She had got under a rock where the snow had not packed too tight, so that she was able to move about a very little. At first she had found a little moss and lichen, but that must have soon given out and she had eaten most of her own wool. Todhunter dug out around her very carefully, till she could walk out without having to plunge through the snow or exert herself. Then he stood well back, kept the dogs away, and let her do as she pleased. Presently the poor old lady walked slowly away from her long prison and began to feed, but she was not really hungry, she had been without food for so long that she was beyond hunger. This ewe, though she had been under the snow for seven weeks, recovered.

CHAPTER XI

CHARLIE STUMP'S HOUNDS

AFTER the snow Todhunter had barely two-thirds of his original flock, and those were all in terrible condition. The ewes had no time to pick up again before lambing time, and many of them slipped their lambs in Nature's instinctive effort to save the mother. That was the worst lambing time that Todhunter had ever known : day after day he went out to find poor, deserted newborn mites wailing pitifully for their mothers : for though there is no more faithful mother than a fell ewe, many of them had not the strength to keep themselves and their lambs, and as with the others Nature saved the mother and wasted the lamb. Todhunter tried to find the ewes belonging to the deserted lambs and to mother the lambs on to them, but it was difficult to manage, and he brought many into his kitchen and reared them on the bottle.

Even the ewes which stuck to their lambs had, many of them, not enough milk to do their lambs properly, and two or three times a day Todhunter went round, his pockets full of bottles of cows' milk, to succour the hungry lambs. As he came into a field sometimes as many as half a dozen lambs, whom he was part-feeding and so knew what he was there for, would leave their ewes, come ma-a-a-ing up to him, butt against his legs, and ask to be fed ; and then when they had had their milk gallop off back to their anxious-eyed mothers.

Not only were there motherless lambs, but there were childless ewes. The previous wet spring and early summer had made it a bad year for rabbits, grouse and other small game, and that meant that now the martens, foxes and eagles were suffering. To do them justice, martens did little or no damage among Todhunter's sheep, but they increased the competition for small game and drove the eagles and especially the foxes more to the pursuit of lambs : the eagles only took an occasional sickly lamb, but there were two litters of cubs in the Black Crags and one of the old ones took a fancy to lambs.

Nearly every morning as soon as he left his cottage Todhunter would hear some old ewe blaring, the unmistakable note of a ewe that has really lost her lamb as distinguished from one that has simply mislaid it. When Todhunter could find the lamb he skinned it and fitted the skin on to one of the lambs in his kitchen, and tried to mother the lamb on to the ewe. It was by no means always successful for the ewes, from their poor condition, were less ready even than usual to suckle a lamb, which, though it had the same smell as their own, yet seemed to have something unnatural about it. Todhunter did his best to get the ewes to take to them, for though a pet lamb is very pretty while it is small, it grows up to be a wratching brute, always leaving the fell, trying to get home to the farm, leading the other sheep astray, and generally being a nuisance to everyone.

As soon as Todhunter found that the foxes were taking his lambs he went to see Charlie Stump. Although some of the lambs that the foxes took could not be laid for certain at their door, there were some that nothing but a fox could have killed. The foxes with very young cubs struck about the shoulder and sucked the blood, when the cubs were a little older they gnawed in and took the heart, lungs and liver ; but the surest sign of all was when the head and tail were bitten off, for nothing but a fox would do that, though what the attraction in the tail is goodness knows.

Stump was the master-huntsman of the local pack of foxhounds : he shared a small farm with his brother, but preferred hunting to shepherding, and did little work on the farm in the winter ; his sheepdog, Lad, was a wonderful example of the effect of the master upon the dog. Very few sheepdogs do much barking, and then usually only when working on cattle or holding up a big mob of sheep, but Lad gave tongue almost incessantly when working and made enough noise for a whole pack of hounds, and funnily enough he had a very deep voice not unlike a foxhound, but that last must have been coincidence for Stump could scarcely have taught him that. Stump spoke to him as though he were a hound and rarely said anything but " Here Lad, here Lad." But Lad seemed to be able to make a pretty good guess whether " here " was intended to mean " come in," or " go out," or what. Lad

was a very fair useful dog without attempting
any of the finer work, but the way he had taken
after the hounds was extraordinary.

Stump and his hounds were much in demand
at the moment, for there was lamb-worrying
at several farms, and most of the hounds were
weary and footsore. However Stump liked
Todhunter and agreed to come the following
day but one, for he had promised on the next
day to go elsewhere. In the spring Stump
had no regular advertised meets, but went where-
ever there was lamb-worrying ; in the winter
his meets were given out in church before
the sermon, and for those sportsmen who
did not attend church, they were also posted
up on the church door.

Besides foxes, Stump hunted the polecats,
which where they were numerous did considerable damage among young lambs. When hunting polecats there was no thought of sport, but
the object was to kill them as quickly as possible.
The polecats took refuge among the crags and
rocks, and they could almost always find a hole
of some sort big enough for them when they
were pressed. At such times Stump lit fires
and bolted them with the smoke.

Stump had once known a case, probably unique, when lambs were worried by a pair of hedgehogs. Hedgehogs were very common in the dales and were most unjustly supposed by many people to milk the cows at pasture, a thing quite impossible on account of the shape of their mouths. The lamb-worrying, however, was authentic : a farmer in Martindale had been slack about dead lambs and this pair of hedge-hogs had taken to feeding on them, and on the cleanings, and from that they came to live ones. They never touched a lamb once fairly on his legs, but they attacked very fresh-born ones at the navel and had killed quite a few in this way.

Stump was much amused because, just before Todhunter had come, a farmer, Harrison, had come to ask for the hounds : Harrison had had a litter of cubs quite close to his farm, and his ducks had wandered regularly within a few hundred yards of the earth. The old vixen paid no attention to the ducks, but Harrison, thinking to make assurance doubly sure, had disturbed the earth. That night the vixen had moved her cubs, and the next day she had taken a duck ; for while her cubs had been close by she had gone farther afield to hunt, but once her cubs had been moved she had no more fears about taking the ducks, and regularly took one every day in broad daylight, for they were shut in at night.

On the morning agreed upon Stump rose before daylight. His appearance would scarcely have passed in a fashionable grass country, for his hunting-dress was an old plum-coloured, long-skirted coat, tweed deerstalker's hat, cord breeches, cloth leggings and fell boots : he carried a stout walking stick in one hand and his hunting crop in the other, and his battered horn in case of accidents was anchored to a buttonhole by a piece of string. He boasted no sanitary kennels, for his was a trencher-fed pack, and the only members of it that he kept himself were a couple of rather decrepit but very staunch old hounds and two and a half couple of fell terriers. These terriers were all shapes and sizes, and all colours : blue, tan, blue and tan, and black and tan, but all were narrow-chested, hard-bitten little devils, and all carried on their grizzled muzzles the honourable scars of battle. They worked rather differently to the white fox terriers, whose job it is to bolt their fox if possible, for these fell terriers, if they could possibly help it, took good care to prevent the fox bolting : they went into an earth with the fixed intention of killing the fox themselves without any interference from the nasty loud-mouthed hounds outside ; and they could expect little help from the men, for most of the earths were in the crags, where nothing short of dynamite could open them.

Stump coupled up two pairs of his terriers but let the odd one run loose, got out his fell pony, and rode up to the village of Fairfield, about a mile from where he lived in the opposite direction to Stonethwaite. He rode up and down the village street blowing his horn, and in this way collected three and a half couple of hounds that appeared from behind divers cottages. Then he rode back towards Stonethwaite ; as he passed each of three farms on the way, he blew his horn and from two of them a hound came and joined him, but the third one was evidently on some private business. At Stone-thwaite he collected two couple in the same way as at Fairfield. As he collected his hounds Stump put a few of them on couples, and most of them before he left Stonethwaite. He jogged

along the track by the beckside and arrived,
at Wancheate Farm at about a quarter to seven.
Some of the hounds started pretty stiffly, but
most of them warmed up fairly well before they
got to the " meet " at Wancheate.

Stump found Todhunter waiting for him with
only two other hardy sportsmen, for Wancheate
was a long way from anywhere. Todhunter
said that he had lost no lambs in the night.

" Then there's nowt te be got down here,"
Stump said. " We'ld best be awa' oop te
yon crags and louze there."

" Ai, that'll be it, didst the' de owt te Fenngill
yeste'day ? "

" Ai, gay good sport, and kilt a fox, but
t'young passon te Crossdale was oot ; he was
verra keen te see t'sport but he kept ower close
te me, and interfered gayly much wi' t'hounds.
We pit oop a hare, seest the', and half t'dogs
was awa' te her track. I rated 'em gayly well
and fetched all back but Trueman, and I'ld
ha' had 'un if it hadna' been for t' passon bein'
in hearin'. Ai, t'passon interfered wi' me ower
much."

This doubtful anecdote did not pass unrivalled
for :

" Didst the' hear o' Tangy's missus ? " asked one of the two members of the field.

" Nay."

" She had triplets."

" Ai."

" Ai, but Tangy had a eowe wi' five lambs and he tolt his missus she should be gayly 'shamed te let an auld Herdwick eowe beat her."

" Nay, the' dinna say ? "

" Ai, but it's true, but Mrs. Tangy cam' oot t'best at t'end o' it for all but yane o' t'lambs deed."

Stump put his pony in a shed and the four of them set off up towards the Crags, the hounds still in the couples. On reaching the bottom of Crag Gate, Stump pointed to a mass of huge crags and ling along to the right saying :

" Yon lakes an ower likely spot, 'tis grand liggin' for an auld fox."

He uncoupled the hounds, who set to work to draw the crags. Stump and the others went on up the Crag Gate, Stump the while encouraging his hounds :

" Hare lying, hare lying, hare lying, ha-a-ards."

A stranger might well have been doubtful as to the exact meaning of his cheer but he was probably not intending any reference to a hare, perhaps he meant " here lying, hey lads," at any rate his voice from long use carried an immense distance, served to let the hounds know where he was, and perhaps to put a fox on foot.

Stump and the others had hardly reached the top of Crag Gate and come out on to Hellaw when the hounds announced that a fox was on the move. Standing on the edge of the cliff the watchers had a good view of the Crags and fell-breast below them. The hounds came close under them, running towards Lake Southermere ; the tall, lean, light-framed, light-coloured hounds made good speed over the broken ground, and their music coming up to the men on top and echoing off the crags would have done credit to fifteen or twenty couple. They ran almost to the edge of Lake Southermere, but then turned and came back lower down the breast and once more passed below Stump and the others. Stump suddenly seized Todhunter's arm saying,

" There goest, seest the' ? t'divil."

Looking where he pointed, Todhunter saw a big dog fox coming up Crag Gate, he was a uniform greyish-red without the black legs often seen on south-country foxes. He came up the gill in long effortless bounds, purposeful and unhurried, came out over the top and away northward over Hellaw. One of the terriers saw him and instantly all five set off in pursuit, yapping at the top of their shrill voices. All, except the odd one, were still in the couples, and they almost strangled themselves and each other in their eagerness. The fox, hearing them, put on an amazing spurt and slipped away out of sight. By and by the terriers returned thoroughly blown and with their red rags hanging right out.

Meanwhile the hounds below kept on with their own fox, or rather, as was more probable, the fox that had come out over Crag Gate was the original one, and they had changed in the crags between the Gate and the lakeside. Stump saw that the hounds would probably go around the corner at the Scarsdale Beck end of the Black Crags and turn up the fellside above the beck, so all four of them hurried along the crag-top to the east.

Soon the hounds were out of sight, and then earshot as well, and by the time that the men reached the fellside above the beck, the hounds had gone as though they had never been. They walked on northwards hoping to see something of them, and after a while luckily fell in with Bellis who had heard the hounds making for Dodd Crags. When they reached Dodd Crags, four miles from Wancheate, they found that hounds had lost their fox. Stump collected three and a half couple of hounds, and had picked up one on the way, but of the others there was no sign. However, they knew their own homes, and would return to them sooner or later, though possibly not for three or four days ; in the meantime they would pick up a meal here and there at a farm or cottage, for anyone would feed a stray hound that called in on his homeward way, or make him a bed somewhere, if he wanted it, till he thought fit to move on.

Stump went back with Todhunter, as did one of the followers as well, and had dinner, and then Stump rode away home on his pony with the remnant of his pack, promising to come another day and chivvy the Wancheate foxes, and Todhunter asked him to come over-night and promised to board him and his hounds. On their way back as each hound passed his

own home he fell out and went in. Late that
evening an old lemon-and-white hound turned
up at the farm. Todhunter gave him a feed
and a bed of bracken, which was the only litter
he ever used, in the cow byre. In the morning
at milking he gave him a sup of milk, and soon
afterwards the hound wandered off.

That morning Todhunter went early to the
high fell to fetch in a ewe and young lamb he
had seen the day before ; he had not long come
out on top of Hellaw and was just climbing out
of the gill when he saw a fox trotting slowly
towards him. The fox had not seen him and
he ducked down out of sight and got hold of
Beth and Meg, the two bitches he had with him,
intending to give the fox a course, for he had
heard yet another ewe blaring on his way up
and was feeling bitter against foxes. He peered
cautiously over the bank of the gill and saw that
it was yesterday's hunted fox coming home,
he was very stiff and still dirty and Todhunter
realised that he would be an easy victim for the
speedy Beth, but that knowledge knocked his
zest for the course out of him and just as the
fox came level with him he showed himself ;
both dogs pulled at their strings and Meg

barked : the old fox had never been nearer death but he stood staring for a moment head up and looking rather grand, and then whisked up his draggled brush and went stiffly away in the same independent, carefree style as if he was as sound as a bell and had nothing more dangerous to fear than a poodle. As Todhunter watched him go he cursed himself for a fool, but consoled himself somewhat with the thought that that fox certainly could not have taken the lamb lost that morning and so probably had never taken any.

A few days later Stump arrived with his hounds in the evening. Todhunter made the hounds up a bed of bracken in a hogg-house which was unused as he always ran his hoggs out on the fell through the winter. In the morning before it was light Stump and Todhunter were around the ewes, they heard the too familiar blare and knew that a lamb had been taken. They waited for daylight and then fetched the hounds out ; Stump put a couple and a half of young hounds in leashes, himself taking a couple and giving Todhunter the other one. He encouraged the other hounds to draw in the field where the ewe was blaring, and they soon struck the night's drag and took it away towards the crags. Stump and Todhunter followed as fast as they could, the hounds in the leashes towing them like horses ; the older hounds hunted the drag slowly and methodically up into the crags, and it was extraordinary that hounds who would hunt so painstakingly would really drive away when they got on terms with their fox. Hounds hunted up to their fox in the crags and went away at a good pace towards the Scarsdale Beck ; Stump and Todhunter then loosed their hounds from the leashes and these raced away to cry.

The tops of the crags were in a thick mist, so, as it was useless to get up on top, the two men walked along the breast after the hounds, who were very soon out of sight. The terriers kept with Stump. The cry of the hounds seemed to swing back right-handed, and at last Stump picked them out filing across the side of Blenthorpe on the far side of the beck : at that distance they showed as only a string of white dots on the face of the screes ; they carried no head but ran one after another in single file, indeed the nature of the ground would not allow of any head. Considering the rough ground they were running at a good pace, but at that distance they appeared to be no more than crawling.

Hounds disappeared over the western shoulder of Blenthorpe and Stump and Todhunter debated whether they should stay where they were in the hope of hounds returning, or descend into the valley and cross the beck. They waited some time, but as they neither saw nor heard any more of hounds they started to cross the valley and go up the other side : they waded through the icy waters of the Scarsdale Beck, where the terriers were forced to swim, and climbed in zigzags up the steep side of the fell. They had gone perhaps half-way up when they heard hounds far above them and looking up, they saw them coming almost straight down out of the mist on the top of the Great Rigg. They were coming at a great pace and rolling small avalanches of shale before them over the loose ground : they checked for a minute or two by the beckside, but presently a few, who had swum across, hit off the line on the opposite bank some little way below where they had checked. They ran pretty fast up to the Black Crags, but there, in amongst the huge boulders at the bottom of the cliff, they hunted more slowly.

Stump and Todhunter went down off Blenthorpe on a fell moving staircase : they got into a bed of small screes and went racing down, every stride nearly doubled in length by the sliding shale, they might have thought that they were shod indeed with seven-league boots though it was no easy thing to keep their balance. The terriers followed after them choking and gasping in the couples. By the time that they reached the Black Crags hounds were marking at the narrow entrance to a deep rocky fastness.

Stump secured the terriers some little way before he got to the earth, and it was as well that he did for as soon as they saw the hounds marking they strained madly at their leads and yapped and squeaked in their excitement ; and in a moment two of the hot little devils, unable to get at the fox, did the next best thing and started a desperate battle between themselves, as they were already fastened together in the couples they were hardly separated. However, Stump got the tangle straightened out and loosed an old black and tan bitch, Grizzle, into the earth, and a minute later another one.

The old dog fox, fat with the fat of many lambs, did not mean to trust himself again to the open : he backed up into a narrow cleft in the rocks where the terriers could only come one at a time, and had to come at him round a corner of the rock. He was taller than the terriers and, standing right over them, he cut them mercilessly about the heads and necks. Even when the terriers got a hold they could not pull the fox around the corner as long as he had strength to brace himself against the jutting rock. The old fox fought for his life savagely and silently, but the men outside could hear the yapping of whichever terrier was not at the moment in possession.

After a while the second terrier, Battle, came out, he was much cut about the face and head, and lay down panting ; but when Stump went to catch him, he tried to dart back into the earth, and Stump only just grabbed him. He put him on a lead and loosed a third terrier, Grip, presently Grip had had enough and came out, and Battle was loosed in once more. Finally Grizzle came out, she was terribly bitten and very done, practically the whole of one ear was missing, and her head, neck and shoulders were covered with blood, not all her own though, and one forefoot was badly bitten, so she had all her wounds before. She lay down and seemed to have no more interest in the proceedings.

Grip was loosed in again. Now there was no yapping from the terriers but a snarling worry that came nearer and nearer to the mouth of the hole. At last Stump, thrusting his arm in up to the shoulder, seized Grip by a hind-leg and hauled her out, with her teeth fast in the fox, and finally Battle came into the light holding on to the other end of the fox. The fox was stone dead, Grizzle had seen to that before she came out. At the sight of the fox the other two terriers went almost mad and the hounds rushed in ; but Grizzle showed no further interest, nor did the hounds once they knew that he was thoroughly dead, for fell hounds do not break up their foxes.

Stump was a little bit anxious about Grizzle's condition, for earlier in the winter he had lost his best terrier in much the same way : he had been at a fox in a rocky earth in the Ravensdale Crags and was still in there at dark when Stump had been compelled to leave, for he could not himself have climbed out of the crags, which were very steep, in the dark. On returning in the morning he found the terrier and the fox both lying outside the earth and both dead. The terrier had killed his fox and dragged him outside and, being very done, had lain down to rest ; it was a frosty night, but the terrier had become very hot fighting in the close earth and the cold coming on top of his exhaustion and loss of blood had killed him.

After leaving Grizzle with Todhunter, who promised to keep her warm, feed her well, and foment her head, Stump got on to his pony and rode off with the rest of his pack. By the evening Grizzle had a head on her like a football, and felt very sick, but the swelling presently went down and in a day or two she was once more as right as rain.

Todhunter lost no more lambs from foxes that spring, but the loss of his sheep in the snow and his bad lambing time had all but ruined him, for his stock had fallen far below the two hundred which really belonged to Sir Ian Stuart. He was quite unable to pay his Ladyday rent, nor did the squire, knowing full well how things were, ask for it.

CHAPTER XII

SPORTS AT ST. JOHNS-IN-THE-VALE

THE annual Whitsun Sports in St. Johns-in-the-Vale attracted enormous interest that year owing to a match between George Dobson and a keeper named Edger which took place there. Dobson had been fairly run down and caught one night when out poaching by Edger, and although a wily lawyer had got him off he felt that his reputation was at stake and he challenged Edger to a match which was arranged to take place at St. Johns-in-the-Vale.

Todhunter was a friend of Dobson's and anyway Dobson always left him some game after a successful night's fowling on Lake Southermere, and so he went to see the match. Besides the match there were two hound trails and a fell race. The old hound trail was the first event and the runners had gone out when Todhunter arrived. The course was about ten miles over a roughly triangular course, starting and finishing in the same field. The two runners went out to about the middle and then, dropping their rags, went one each way so that they would arrive in the field at about the same time and leave the trail fairly fresh all along. Presently the runner who had taken the last half appeared and a minute or two later the other, but the latter stopped in the next field to the starting field.

The starter then called up the hounds : they came up led by their owners or, to be more exact, hauling their owners along, for most of them pulled like Shire horses, straining from their hocks and scarcely putting their forefeet on the ground at all, while their owners leant right back against them as they walked. When the rugs, which most of them wore, were removed, they looked rum-looking devils to anyone used to a grass-country foxhound. They were nearly all clipped all over and trained very light. The clipping changed their colour so that the black became blue and the tan lemon. One or two had brindled marks and argued the presence of some greyhound ancestor in their pedigrees, and one was all red fawn leaving no doubt about the matter : a few of them were ticked and showed pointer blood ; the pointers had been used in the old days to get nose into the fell hounds, and the trail hounds, kept very much to themselves and inbred, showed more of the characteristics of the old fell hounds than did the hounds then in the fell packs.

The clipping accentuated their lightness of flesh, and all had staring ribs and prominent hip bones, but not from lack of food, for they were fed like game-cocks, often literally, for some of them were fed on specially prepared bread like cock-bread as well as fruit lough, eggs, fish, cowheel jelly, and goodness knows what besides ; but no red meat, for that would drive them to water on a hot day. They were not all of a type : most of them high on the leg, deep-chested, and light-loined looked a little bit like pointers, but that was largely due to their clipped skins and tails, which last they carried low rather than over their backs like foxhounds, but some of them were long and lathy of the fell hound type. Nearly all had beautiful clean-boned straight legs, and clean, close feet.

When the hounds had been brought into line and their rugs taken off, an official went down the line marking each on the shoulder with a blue stain, lest some wily customer should slip his hound in half-way. Then their collars were taken off and their owners held them firmly by their necks and loins, or anywhere else where they thought that they could get a good grip. The runner, who had been waiting in the next field, came over the wall and in towards the starting line : when he was within about fifty yards, and the aniseed and paraffin was so strong that a person with a heavy cold could easily smell it, the starter who had been holding up his hat dropped it.

The hounds were loosed and raced away past the runner, who picked up his rag. Although some of the hounds passed within a few feet of the runner and his stinking rag, none of them paid the least attention to him. Many of the hounds had been making a great row while they were held in the line, but as soon as they started to run they stopped their cry and ran absolutely mute, except two or three who gave tongue for the first fifty or hundred yards : all were mute before they reached the wall. They went over the wall in a solid wave, fifteen or twenty nearly abreast, for there were over sixty starters ; one or two flew the wall clean, many others gave it a contemptuous kick-back, and the rest ran up the side like cats and sprang from the top.

The hounds went racing away up the fellside and out of sight, but before they disappeared a nearly white hound had gone into a twenty yards' lead of anything and was identified by the crowd as Helvellyn, the favourite. His sire, Glenderamakin, had been about the fastest trail hound ever seen, but a terribly bad finisher : he had once arrived on the field after the others had gone, his owner had obtained permission to slip him, and although he was started three minutes late yet he won : he had been known to be a mile in front of anything as fresh as paint and yet be beaten, it was not that he tired but he seemed to get bored and stopped and waited about for the others to come up, and after a while off he would go again and be soon way out in front once more, perhaps only to stop again. It just depended on whether he happened to be racing at the finish or fooling about, whether he won or not. Everything was tried to make him run right through but without success.

Helvellyn was bred from a bitch who, though

no good herself, was of the same litter as a good dog, Hartside. Hartside had been famed for his cunning, he paid little attention to the trail but ran always on the inside watching his opportunity to make a cut. He was as good a finisher as Glenderamakin was bad ; the moment he heard the first whistle up would go his head, and he would come as hard as he could lay legs to the ground absolutely dead straight over or through anything, and if he was within striking distance when the whistles started it was a fair bet that he would win. Helvellyn, though he had not Glenderamakin's brilliance nor Hartside's cunning, was a fair, good dog and more reliable than either.

After what seemed an age, but was really only a few minutes, the leading hound appeared running along the fellside high above the spectators. He was no more than a white dot, but the crowd mostly agreed that it was Helvellyn, though the hope was probably father to the thought. A couple of hundred yards behind the leader came two together, then another gap, and then all the rest strung out for a mile or more. The ruck was nearly a hundred yards wide, and bore convincing testimony to the power of the aniseed. All were going at a great pace. They raced for nearly two miles along the fellside, in and out of three gills, and finally disappeared once more over a shoulder of the fell.

When next Helvellyn appeared he was coming down off the fell, there were three others fairly close behind, and they came down the fellside like flames, racing down the breast with long sweeping strokes and travelling at a terrific speed : the light-coloured hounds against the brown heather looked like seagulls slipping out of the sky against a dark cloud.

Helvellyn disappeared for a moment behind a wall and then came sailing over it : the others flicked up on top and over. By this time there were forty or more in sight all tearing down the fellside like a waterfall. They went out of sight behind some trees and came up the flat valley land to the finish ; they were to finish over a lane and between a couple of posts in the finishing field. At the far side of the field beyond the lane a man was looking out and before long he waved his hat to show that they were coming.

Then bedlam broke loose, almost everyone

knew in his own mind that Helvellyn was leading,
but everyone that had a hound in the trail appeared
to hope that the leader, or at any rate one of the
first few, was his, for all the lot, over sixty of
them, began to whistle and shout as though
their lungs must burst ; most of them had
different whistles or calls which their hounds
were supposed to know, and the noise was
terrific.

Helvellyn appeared in the field beyond the lane
and came striding along with long, slow strokes
that covered an enormous quantity of ground.
His jaws were hanging open and his tongue
out, indeed his tongue hung out so far, and
flapped up and down in time with his long
uncut ears, that as he came straight towards
the crowd his tongue looked rather like a third
pink ear. He made no sound as he came up
but not so his owner, whose voice rose high
above the rest.

" Hey, hey, hey, lad, hey, hey, hey."

Helvellyn came striding down to the lane
which was fenced by two laid fences : he stood
well back and rocketed over into the lane,
changed feet once and sailed out into the finishing
field. It would have been a grand performance

even for a fresh hound, but for one that had gone
ten miles over the fells in half an hour it was
nothing short of wonderful, and was greeted
by a mighty cheer from the crowd and a shout
of :

"Ai, did'st the' see 'un lep t'lonning ?"

His owner continued to shout, "Hey, hey,"
at the top of his voice, and held out a small shallow
tin full of nicely minced tripe. Helvellyn came
racing past the posts and into the crowd looking
for his owner, on seeing him he rushed up to him
and thrust his face into the proffered tin : he
was so blown that he could scarcely close his
mouth but he choked the tripe down somehow,
at the same time half-filling the tin with the
sweat that rained from his jaws : his ribs were
heaving up and down, and he looked thinner
even than before he went out so that one might
almost have feared that his ribs would break
through his shaven skin.

The other hounds came up in ones and twos
and bunches, leaped or banked quickly over the
lane fences, but none in Helvellyn's matchless
style : very few of them smeused. There was
a close race for third place and the owner of
the fourth, besides screaming at the top of his

voice, flapped his hound's rug violently up and down, but in vain, for his hound was beaten a neck for the third place. Everyone continued to shout or whistle till he had got his own hound and some of them did not come in for ten minutes or more. Each hound as he came in was given some dainty from a tin or a piece of paper, and some of them, missing their owners, tried to get their faces into the nearest tin or piece of paper, and were abusively repulsed.

The judge had six men with him who were to catch the first six past the post : he pointed them out to the catchers as they passed, and the man whose job it was to catch that hound, third, or fourth, or whichever number it was, dashed away and keeping sight of it took it at once from its owner as soon as the collar was on, and led it back to the judge, where it was claimed by the owner and the prize money taken. That was the only possible way of judging, for the hounds carried no numbers, and the judge could scarcely be expected to know all sixty by sight.

As soon as the excitement of the hound trail was over the open fell race was started. A man with a white flag had already taken up his position on the crest of the fell several hundred feet above the sports field, and indeed had it not been for his flag he would scarcely have been distinguishable from the many rocks which were scattered over the fell ; the course was around him and back. The fourteen starters then lined up, each was clad simply in a zephyr, shorts, socks and light shoes with studs or spikes. At the fall of the starter's flag they ran across the field, over a wall, and started up the fell breast. They were soon strung out almost in single file and the fell was so steep that only in places were they able to run ; they toiled up the slope most of them with their hands on their knees to give them an extra push, and broke into a trot wherever possible. Three of the runners were soon hopelessly out of it and gave up before they had gone half way-up. At last the leader reached the man with the flag, went around behind him taking his ticket as evidence that he had really been up, and started down : he came running and leaping down more than three times as fast as he had gone up and had greatly increased his lead before the second had reached the top.

The second, however, was far from done with,

he came down in the most reckless fashion rapidly overhauling the leader and it seemed that if he could keep his feet he must pass him, but just when he drew level he took the most appalling fall and skidded yards along on his chest. He was up in a moment and coming on as hard as ever in his attempt to reduce the lead which his fall had given the other. He might have won yet had he not fallen again near the bottom and lost more ground than he could possibly catch up ; however, he limped in a good second, and the others came tailing in after him.

After the fell race came the puppy trail ; the inexperienced eager puppies made a deal more noise while held in the starting line than had the old hounds, and on being started one stopped for nearly half a minute playing around the man with the drag till he was driven away by his owner, but he only went a field before coming back : another also gave up and came back, while the rest went on out of sight. The puppy trail was shorter than the old hounds', being only seven or eight miles, and it gave an excellent finish, feet only dividing the first four, and they passed and repassed each other several times in the last two fields.

The Dobson-Edger match, which as supposedly the best part of the entertainment had been kept till the last, fell very flat. Dobson was not only past his best but the conditions of the match were quite unsuitable to him : his greatness lay in his knowledge of the rough fell country and in his ability to get over it in the dark ; when chased by a keeper he was able to choose his own ground which was usually the roughest that he could find, and he was not in the habit of racing straight up several hundred feet of steep but comparatively smooth fell. The result was that although he was a good enough runner, as witness his race with Burton's trap to his brother's farm over the small matter of the stolen goose, he was no match for Edger in the straight climb up the fellside, and when he realised that the slight superiority that he probably had in coming down would never reduce the big lead that Edger was getting on the way up, he gave up and turned back.

After the match Edger was very proud of himself but for all that he was never able to catch Dobson poaching again, although he tried hard enough and Dobson in no way curtailed his activities.

CHAPTER XIII

THIEF IN THE NIGHT

By midsummer Beth had become an almost perfect fell sheepdog, well trained and very, very wise. Todhunter, by patience had at last got her pretty easy to move on her sheep, she had learnt the left and right whistles, and she worked almost entirely on the whistles except very close at hand and would obey the whistles as far as she could hear them, which except in a strong head wind was an enormous distance, well over half a mile ; and, as she had been slowly trained in such a way as to develop her instinct and intelligence, she could work well enough when she could neither hear a whistle nor see her handler and it was nothing extraordinary for her to work for half an hour without another order, and be a mile or more away.

Naturally a powerful forcing bitch, after the bad weather when sheep were weak, Beth gained experience with soft sheep, which could not be driven by force but must be coaxed by tact. A soft sheep if forced would lose all heart, and perhaps lie down, and once in that state nothing could move it, for it seemed no longer to care what happened to it. So with soft sheep Beth learnt to keep out wide and, when the sheep grew discouraged, stop and lie down or weave about them, till they would at last go slowly on after the others. Ewes with young lambs were the same, if the dog came too close they would turn round and make a stand, and an old fell ewe will fight sometimes to the death for her lamb ; but Beth, keeping well off, learnt to coax the old women along. Though she gained in tact and experience Beth never lost her power, and she could stand up to a stubborn sheep, and run in and meet it as it charged, for she was afraid of nothing.

The squire once witnessed an example of Beth's power ; he had been out deer-coursing alone with only two bitches, Valkyrie and her daughter Shield : he was out early to avoid the heat of the day and got a long slip at a big hart. Valkyrie and Shield had a real doing, they were both always very hot and went with terrific dash throughout a long course, taking one or two heavy falls on the steep ground. The hart was a big one and they were rather small even for bitches, always a deal smaller than the dogs, and they were again and again thrown off. The hart was at last brought to bay in the Wancheate Gill but he twice broke bay, moving down-stream each time, and was taken not far from the Black Crags.

Valkyrie and Shield had done more than enough for one day and Shield was a bit knocked about so there was no thinking of another course, and anyway the ground had been thoroughly disturbed. Ian, who had run hard and was pretty blown, sat down for a while to rest himself and his bitches. Presently he heard Todhunter whistling to his dogs and, on climbing out of the gill, saw him coming with a big mob of sheep to a small walled fold near the top of Crag Gate. Ian went over to the fold to talk to him.

Todhunter had gathered up all his higher fell flock and after getting them into the fold he put them through the sorter, a narrow race which only admitted one sheep at a time and was closed by a gate which, hinged at the far end from the race, moved diagonally across its mouth so that the sheep coming through the race could be deflected two ways as the gate was moved, either out of the fold altogether or into the other half of it. Beth, Meg and Jess held the sheep up into the race while Todhunter worked the sorter. He passed the tup lambs into the small fold and all the old sheep and gimmer lambs out once more on to the fell, where they all quickly wandered off except the mothers of the tup lambs, and these Todhunter sent his dogs to drive away a little after the others. Then he called his dogs in and let out the tup lambs, which he casually explained to Ian he wanted for market, and he saw no sense in bringing the mothers down as well as they would only hang about the farm looking for their lambs and not return to fell, nor be too keen about stopping there if they were sent back, as they would likely return where they had last seen their lambs.

As soon as the lambs were let out they made the most determined efforts to get to their mothers, and no sheep, not even tups, are as difficult to manage as lambs, let alone when they can see and hear their mothers. Beth was worth three

of Meg and Jess put together and, indeed, without
her the work would have been impossible.
Yet with her assistance, and to Ian's amazement,
Todhunter drove his lambs off down Crag Gate
without one breaking away or one ewe joining
them ; or perhaps it would be truer to say Beth
did it with the assistance of Todhunter and
Meg and Jess.

Ian knew something about dogs for they were
the only labour employed on his farms, but as
he said when describing Beth's performance to
Ursula :

" If I had not seen it done, I would not have
believed it possible." And indeed she could
scarcely have been more highly tried.

Beth, when she got her full growth, was
quite a tall bitch, but she was always light-framed,
although her long thick coat made her look
heavier than she really was. She had really
good speed and although that was of no very
great importance, it was useful at times when it
was a near thing about heading off a sheep that
had broken away and was attempting to join
another lot. She was nearly all black with just
a little white about her muzzle, on her chest,
and at the end of her bushy tail, and she had

one white forefoot; she had no tan. Beth's head was something like old Bright's, wide in the skull, with long fine jaws and a dish face ; but unlike her father she had big prick ears set high on her head, and these with her fine jaws gave her a frightfully sharp expression. She had a grand low style, wide on her turns, but was more than a little inclined to be over-hard on her sheep.

Besides her general excellence Beth had enormous, and indeed almost unnatural, resolution and when sent out to do anything never came back until it was done unless Todhunter actually called her off. If he sent her out for sheep where no sheep were she would go on and on till she found some somewhere, so he had to be careful, and if he sent her out to fetch sheep or the like, not realising how difficult it would be for her, and if then he called her off before she had done the job, she always came in looking crestfallen as if she thought that she must have done something wrong, and worse than that she would sulk and would often do no more real work for the rest of the day. Todhunter, once he realised this peculiarity, took care not to disappoint her if possible, and if he found it was impossible for her to shift the sheep as he had hoped, as, for instance, if they were stuck in the crags, he would get her to move them somewhere else, or get some other sheep even though it were to his own disadvantage ; so that when she had done it and he called " That'll do " Beth would leave her sheep and come in happily.

This frightful determination of Beth's to get done what she considered her job, no matter what obstacle stood in her way, was destined to have a great effect not only on her own life, but on that of her master as well. There were two pieces of work which Beth did which were responsible for putting ideas into Todhunter's head.

On the first occasion Todhunter was drunk, this was by no means a common occurrence, but one night of unusually bad pain from his back he sat up over a fire all night drinking whisky, and in the morning when he went out to attend to his cows he was very unsteady on his legs : he blundered over Beth and almost fell, as he recovered his balance he swore at her :

" Get away, Beth."

Beth was unused to seeing him drunk and could

not understand what was wrong nor what he meant her to do, so she came up closer to him, and again got in his way.

"Get away, Beth" Todhunter repeated angrily, "Beth, get away, get away out."

Beth disappeared through the door and out of the yard towards the fell, going as hard as she could travel.

Todhunter presently, with the help of a short sleep and then the water-trough, sobered up ; it was then about midday. He remembered cursing at Beth and regretted it, and, when he could not find her, he became anxious and went up towards the fell to look for her. As he went across the fell-intake, Todhunter looked over the fell in the hope of seeing something of Beth, and was surprised to see no sheep at all in sight on the lower fell-breast. As he came up to the gate he found the reason, for the whole, or practically the whole, of his lower-fell flock was jammed against the wall and gate, and beyond them ranged Beth up and down, up and down, holding them together and waiting for her master.

Beth had taken the "Beth, get away" for a cast out order, and had acted accordingly.

Then one day in the autumn when Todhunter was on one of his weekly visits to Stonethwaite with his eggs and butter, he noticed that some of his lower-fell sheep had got to the eastern end of the Black Crags, and appeared likely to wander up the fell beyond the Crags. The next day he went with his dogs to shift the sheep back towards Crag Gate. He himself, starting from the beckside, made his way along under the crags, letting his dogs run in the crags above him. A shearling that was high up near the top of the crags missed its feet and fell, it came bounding down like a tennis ball, hitting a ledge and then bounding off to hit again lower down and bounce off once more. It fell a great height in this way and finally finished up on a fairly wide shelf of grass. To Todhunter's utter amazement it got up after perhaps a minute, apparently no whit the worse. At every bounce it had landed on its side where the thick wool acted like a sort of cushion; had it once fallen on its head or even hind end, the shock must have killed it.

After a while Todhunter had collected about fifteen sheep, and Beth was working out of sight up in the crags ; as she did not appear for some time he realised that she must have got stuck with some sheep, and he sent Jess up to help her. Presently Jess returned to him but there was still no sign of Beth. As Todhunter could not see what was happening he could not well give Beth another order; he knew that she would not hurt the sheep and as she did not like to be called off, he went on with the others and left her to get on as best she could. He took the sheep that he had nearly to the Wancheate Gill, left them there, and went down to his dinner. After dinner he was busy and still did not bother about Beth, but when after milking she had not come he went to look for her. It was then five o'clock and had been scarcely ten when he had last seen her in the crags.

As soon as Todhunter got over the stile in the wall of the fell-intake he saw five sheep with Beth lying beyond holding them up. One or two of the sheep were still blowing a little, and so they could have only just arrived. The sheep had got fast in the crags and Beth had been seven hours shifting them and bringing them down. She had seen Todhunter go home, and she had brought them as near home as she could get ; when she was stopped by the wall she had lain down to wait till her master should come and let them through. She never doubted but that he would come.

That day's work, though remarkable enough in itself, was to have still more remarkable results for, coming on top of Beth's gathering on the morning that Todhunter was drunk, it was to be the cause of Beth's start on a career of crime.

John Todhunter by this time was probably a bit queer, he had lived for many years entirely alone with his animals, he had had repeated bouts of frightful pain in his back and had drunk a great deal of bad whisky to deaden it, and even when he was in no pain he lived always under the shadow of the fear of it. He quite justifiably resented the extremely shabby advantage that Burton had taken over him in the selling of the hay and he had rather brooded over his wrong and hoped for a way of reprisal. He now thought that he saw in Beth a possible means of getting his own back, which was the more attractive to him in that it would give him an extraordinary chance to develop Beth's talents.

The day after Beth had brought the sheep

down from the crags Todhunter took her alone and went up Crag Gate on to the high fell, he then went in a north-easterly direction till he was about the same distance from the Crag Gate and the eastern end of the Black Crags, and then seeing eight sheep more or less together he sent Beth out to gather them. Beth soon brought them up to him, and Todhunter, by whistling her rather round them to the left, got her to drive them on past him towards the Crag Gate. Todhunter then walked south towards the Crags, but kept Beth driving her sheep south-west towards the Gate.

As Beth got farther and farther away from her master she began to hesitate, for it always rather went against her nature to drive sheep away ; but Todhunter kept encouraging her with whistle and voice to drive on, and whenever she got a bit around her sheep he whistled her back behind them and once more bade her drive on. Finally when he got on to a bit of a rise, whence he could see to the gate which was yet nearly half a mile to his right front, he stopped but kept Beth driving on. Beth got up to the gate and drove the sheep down, but she hesitated before going down herself and looked back at

Todhunter, but he kept whistling her to drive on " Whe-whu-who, whe-whu-who," and after a moment she went down after her sheep.

As soon as Beth was out of sight Todhunter ran as fast as he could straight to the top of the Crags, whistling " drive on " at intervals. When he got to the top he peered cautiously over and having assured himself that Beth was still driving her sheep down the gill, he turned and went as quickly as he could down to the beckside, and then home by the track. He wanted to get home in time to meet Beth with the sheep, but as he had more than twice as far to go he had to hurry : he took great care lest she should catch sight of him on his way up the track, and so be tempted to hold the sheep towards him instead of straight on towards the farm.

Beth was much worried by the whole thing, her instinct and indeed training was, when in doubt, to hold the sheep towards her handler, but on this occasion the only clear thing in an otherwise puzzling situation was that the one thing that Todhunter apparently did not want was to have the sheep brought to him. Beth believed that whatever happened Todhunter could do no wrong, and when she got out of sight and hearing of him and was thrown on her own initiative she knew of nothing to do but to keep straight on and drive the sheep home ; and yesterday's work, which had evidently pleased Todhunter, being fresh in her memory, she was the more inclined to do so. She could not know that what had pleased Todhunter had been her resolution in sticking to the sheep rather than fetching them home, for Beth's simple mind dealt not in reasons but in facts.

Beth had no easy task driving the sheep down on her own, for they were unwilling to leave their heath and fought back the whole time, one or two of the more determined ones continually breaking past her ; but she held them on and being anxious as to whether she was doing the right thing she was out of temper and inclined to be rough with them. Her progress was slow, however, and she repeatedly stopped to look and listen for her master. The result was that Todhunter beat her to the farm.

When Beth reached the intake gate, which Todhunter had previously left open, she came on through the intake and brought the sheep into the field behind the farm. There Todhunter met her and, without in any way making a fuss

of her, he showed her very plainly that she had
done right. She came up to him a bit doubtfully,
her ears moving nervously, but at the first " Good
lass, Beth," her ears flicked back and she
" laughed."

The next day Todhunter repeated the lesson.
Beth knew what she was to do and drove confidently off home. As soon as he saw that she
was going Todhunter gave no more orders,
but at once went off home the other way and
as before met Beth and the sheep at the
farm.

The following day he did nothing with Beth,
but in the afternoon he took Jess and Meg
and drove the sheep back to the high fell. He
gathered up a dozen more and drove them off
the fell to the east, leaving them close to the
Scarsdale Beckside a mile north of the Black
Crags. The next morning early Todhunter
took Beth up to where he had left the sheep,
going by way of the beckside. He found
five of them not far from where he had left them,
the other seven had already gone back to their
heath. He sent Beth back with them the way
they had come, and himself went back by the
Crag Gate. Beth was back before him, and was

waiting for him with the sheep. The next day he did nothing with her, but that night he took her up Crag Gate, gathered six sheep off the high fell, and sent her off back through the Gate with them, himself going around by the beckside. Beth did the job all right in the dark, and Todhunter decided that she would do, for he was reluctant to do too much with her for fear of making her careless.

The next night Todhunter put Beth to the test. He set off about midnight and took his gun with him that, if he should meet anyone, he might be thought to be merely poaching, for he had no intention of being seen by anyone with sheep, whatever happened. He forded the Scarsdale Beck, where Beth had to swim part of the way, and then climbed up the screes of Blenthorpe on to the Great Rigg, and thence over on to the sheep pasture beyond. In the dark Todhunter could see no sheep so, afraid to waste time, he sent Beth out to see what she could find. Scarcely ten minutes later she returned with sixteen, the grey sheep suddenly looming up like ghosts out of the dark. Todhunter shed out seven and left them behind but he set off homewards with the other nine.

He had not gone a hundred yards before he sent
Beth on with them alone, and himself made his
way down to the lakeside and thence homewards.

Todhunter anticipated that Beth's greatest
difficulty would be in getting the sheep
across the Scarsdale Beck and he hoped to
get them there about dawn, so that in case of
difficulty they would have the light to help them.
If anything he wished to err on the side of being
too early, so he allowed Beth a speed of one
and a half miles an hour, he thought that that
would be pretty good going in the dark and
over rough country unknown to her, as the
usual speed of travelling sheep is about two
miles an hour, but against that was the fact
that two miles an hour allowed for not hurrying
the sheep and Todhunter did not suppose that
Beth would be very particular about that.

Todhunter arrived at the place where the
Scarsdale Beck emptied into Lake Southermere
nearly an hour before dawn ; he turned and
walked up the beckside but neither saw nor heard
anything of Beth or the sheep. He sat down
to wait at the point where he thought they
would probably come, and he felt sure that he

would hear them coming down over the loose screes. He was in good time and hardly expected them for a while, but the time in the dark passed very slowly, and after a while, when he heard nothing, he began to get anxious ; and when at last, after what seemed the longest hour he had ever spent, it began to grow light, he got really worried : he strained his eyes through the dusk up the hillside, but saw nothing ; he got up and walked some way downstream that he might see the far side of a spur that obstructed his view, but as far as he could see, nothing moved on the northern face on Blenthorpe. Really anxious now, he forded the beck and started to climb up to the Great Rigg.

After an hour's climb, Todhunter reached the top, but though he saw some sheep grazing on the southern slopes there was no sign of Beth. He walked for half a mile along under the brow, but, still seeing nothing, he turned wearily homewards. Half-way down he heard a raven's croak and saw the raven dropping out of the sky in a spiral dive, every few hundred feet checking himself and peering downwards, finally he alighted beneath a crag and Todhunter saw that a dead sheep was lying there ; he turned aside to examine the sheep and saw by the marks that it was one of Burton's ; it was a ewe and only recently dead, in fact almost certainly in the night, for it had not been touched except for an eye already picked out by the raven which he had seen go to it. Todhunter thought that it had most likely been one of Beth's and, wondering if the sheep had somehow stampeded and Beth had lost them in the dark, he went on home.

* * * * *

Beth had known well enough that Todhunter would not have taken her at night on strange ground and used the whole time the utmost caution if there was not something extraordinary afoot. She was very sensitive to Todhunter's moods and realised that he was unusually strung up, and so as soon as he left her to get on by herself with the sheep, she drove them with even more than her usual fire. When she came to the top of the Great Rigg she had some difficulty with them, for she did not know the country nor the best ways down, and as sheep rarely came down on to the north side where there was no grass, they had no trods down.

From the top of the Rigg the slope down the

north side appeared in the dark like an enormous abyss, in the bottom of which far, far below the light of the stars was here and there reflected from the surface of the beck. The sheep, who hated moving in the dark, especially over country they did not know, were probably also really afraid, but Beth was determined that they should go down. She got them above some screes that looked to her less steep than elsewhere, hounded them up together, and then drove in first on one flank and then the other. She was no longer a quiet sheepdog but a raging demon, she flew backwards and forwards snapping at the sheep's quarters, her teeth clicking together, and even pulling out wool ; she did not actually bite them but she did everything but.

At last the sheep, thinking that the danger behind them was worse than that before, went down on to the screes ; directly they started down Beth followed up her advantage hard and the whole nine with Beth at their heels raced madly down the screes, the shale flying in an avalanche around them. The side of Blenthorpe was not one straight slope but was cut downwards by deep gills and bolstered up with crags, so that nothing that had not wings could go straight

down, but Beth held the sheep downwards the
whole time, only allowing them to go along
the side when it was absolutely necessary. In
the dark and hurry one ewe was shouldered
over a crag, that was the dead ewe which Todhunter saw, but Beth never saw her fall and kept
on with the others.

The sheep were soon so blown that they could
no longer gallop, but all resistance was knocked
out of them and they walked quietly along
whichever way Beth drove them. They had
come so fast down the first part of the screes
that in a very short time they reached the edge
of the beck. They came to a place where the
near side was very rocky and rather shallow, so
the sheep were all but in the water before they were
aware of it. They made some sort of a stand,
but they were jaded, and Beth was so determined
that there could be but one finish and in they all
went. Once in the swift current under the
far bank some of them attempted to turn back
and climb out on the same side as they went
in, but Beth met them in the face, drove them
back and easily prevented them landing. When
all were across Beth swam over and collected
them, for a few had landed some way downstream.

She drove them across the two small fields through the open gates and into the farmyard. There she lay down to await her master.

As Todhunter came into the yard and saw Beth lying opposite the sheepfold entrance guarding her eight sheep, he was amazed to find them already there, but that was not the only time that Beth's extraordinary determination made a fool of him and upset calculations based on a life experience of sheep and sheepdogs.

Todhunter at once set to work to alter the marks of the stolen sheep. Burton's marks were a slit at near ear and upper fold bit far, that is, the near ear was partly slit up from the tip, and a triangular piece was cut out of the top side of the far ear by folding it double and snicking off a corner with the shears : the wool mark was a stroke down the far ribs. Todhunter with the shears, which he heated in a bucket of burning peat, altered the triangular fold bit to a square key cut and cut off the lower corner of the slit ear ; then he rubbed a little green salve over the new wounds to assist the burning to heal them quickly. He renewed the wool mark up the far ribs and continued it along the back to the tail, this was easy enough, for Burton, and indeed nearly all the fell farmers, used the same red wool mark. The sheep now bore Todhunter's lower-fell marks ; lower half near ear, upper key cut far, and a bugle horn wool mark on the far side. Then he took Beth and drove them up to the western end of the black Crags, close to the lakeside, and left them there.

Two nights later Todhunter stole seven more of Burton's sheep, but took them from a spot nearly a mile to the south-east of the place where he had taken the others. The business went off without a hitch and he changed their marks as before and put them with the others up in the crags.

Although the stolen sheep fought back continually towards their own heaths they were held up, first by the walls of Todhunter's enclosed land, and then by the beck. One or two of them got over the walls all right for they were all dry walls and for solidity were built sloping towards the top, being quite three feet wide at the bottoms and only a foot or eighteen inches at the tops. It is almost incredible the way some fell sheep can deal with these walls, hoicking up on top in much the same way that an Irish hunter deals with a stone-faced bank, and if they are broken down, lambs a few days, aye and a few hours old, will follow their dams over quite decent gaps, but then it is not an unknown thing for a fell sheep to jump timber as high as a low gate, going clean over the top with hardly a rap. To stop the sheep jumping them, most of the walls had bigger stones on top that jutted out and prevented the sheep getting a foothold on top, but these stones were always rather liable to fall off. However, if they got over the walls, the beck stopped them and they had no mind to swim home. Todhunter kept a watch on them and drove them back up into the crags as often as they wandered down.

Todhunter did not believe that the sheep would be missed until Burton came to gather his whole flock for the autumn dip. Even if he happened to notice the absence of one or two of the stolen sheep, which was not likely, unless he really set out to look for them, he would only imagine that they had wandered away a little or were simply out of sight in some hollow or gill.

When Todhunter had sold the fifteen stolen sheep to the wholesale buyer in the autumn he would be well repaid for the advantage Burton had taken of him over the hay ; but once he had started stealing it was not so easy for him to stop, he wanted money for he always lived a hand-to-mouth existence and he was particularly badly off after the loss of so many sheep and lambs as a result of the winter's bad weather.

CHAPTER XIV

BETH HELD UP

TODHUNTER made no more raids on Burton's farm, for that was too easy, and therefore too risky, for he realised that the more difficult appeared the stealing, the less likely would he be to be suspected. He made raids two or three times a week on nearly all the neighbouring farms which he could reach by the fells without having to cross a road ; he became more careless about the marks and took sheep if it was possible to change the ear marks, even though very roughly, into one or other of his own ear marks. The wool marks he did not trouble about at all, for as they had been last marked immediately after clipping when the wool was short, now that the wool had grown to its full length the marks had become rather faint, and Todhunter with a knife plucked and broke off the ends of the marked wool, and then rubbing dirt over the place to hide where the old mark had been removed, he put on one of his own marks to match whichever of his ear marks he had made.

Todhunter further increased Beth's natural inclination to shyness by taking her in the daytime where he thought that he would meet people, and then on seeing anyone he told Beth to clear out; at first she was puzzled, but Todhunter, who could make any dog, let alone Beth, understand almost anything, soon made it clear to her to get out of sight and that the more easily on account of her deer-poaching experience. In a day or two Beth learnt to clear out unbidden as soon as she saw anyone, and when they had gone on out of sight she would turn up again.

On each excursion Todhunter took as a rule about four or five sheep, he never took less than three, for one or two would have been more awkward for Beth to drive than four or five, and he rarely took more than six lest their absence might be missed.

As every venture was entirely successful Todhunter became more confident and went further afield till it was no longer possible for Beth to bring the sheep home before daylight.

For a while all went well for the country was
so wild and sparsely inhabited that on the high
fells Beth might often have done the whole
business in broad daylight and never have
been seen ; and Beth, when driving stolen sheep
home, always kept to the wildest parts of the
fells because she was perfectly aware that she
must avoid men and not be seen, and also the
valleys where the farms were, being richer grass,
were mostly enclosed for cattle and lambing
ewes, so that she had to keep to the unfenced
fells to get along at all.

Todhunter usually went out along the route
that he expected that Beth would use on her
return, but after starting her off with the sheep,
he returned whichever way he thought quickest
and best, and so often he got home long before
Beth and would have to wait till she arrived.
When she brought sheep from one of the farms
to the north, Beth always brought them down
off Hellaw by way of the Wancheate Gill and
down Crag Gate. Todhunter, except on the
nights when he intended Beth to bring sheep
down it, stopped up Crag Gate by rolling two
large rocks into the narrowest and steepest part
of the gill : these rocks absolutely prevented

any sheep passing up off the lower fell below the cliff on to the top of Hellaw ; so the only way that sheep taken from the north could return home was by way of the eastern end of the Black Crags and along the Scarsdale Beck-side. As the sheep had all come down the Crag Gate it took them some time to find the other way, and Todhunter, by almost daily gathering out the eastern end of the Black Crags, took good care that no sheep got round the end and on to Hellaw.

One Tuesday night Todhunter took Beth on to the top of Saddleback Fell some seven miles from Wancheate, and, after rounding up five Swaledale ewes belonging to a farmer named Edwards, sent Beth off home with them. Todhunter went back the best way that he could and arrived some two hours before dawn, he knew, however, that Beth, keeping to the high unenclosed fells, could not do it under nine or ten miles, and he hardly expected her before dawn. He hoped that she would at least cross the Great Rigg before daylight, as once on the northern slopes of Blenthorpe there was little chance of her being seen, while as long as she remained on the southern side where Burton

grazed his sheep there was always a risk that
Burton or one of his sons, while shepherding
there might see her.

As soon as it was light Todhunter anxiously
scanned the slopes of Blenthorpe for any sign
of Beth and her sheep, but in vain. As time
passed he became more and more worried,
and vainly attempted to occupy himself and pass
the time working about his yard. He hated
to leave her up on the fell where some accident
might have befallen her, but on the other hand
he was afraid to go and look for her : if she had
fallen in with anyone, he, by appearing, would
only incriminate himself, when, as hardly anyone
knew Beth by sight, there was little chance of her
being recognised as his dog, and if left alone
she would almost certainly very soon make
her escape from almost anywhere and return
home.

As the afternoon passed Todhunter's anxiety
for his dog gradually overcame his fear for
himself ; he milked and attended to his few
cows early, and set off over the Great Rigg and
across Blenthorpe, but although he looked most
anxiously and kept to the ridges where he could
see farthest, he saw no sign of Beth. He went

out about six miles and then, going out of his way another two miles, he came to Dobson's cottage and called on him, ostensibly to tell him that he had seen a fine flight of duck on Lake Southermere, but really to have some excuse for going that way in case Beth had been seen by anyone who, not knowing her, might yet, if he saw Todhunter in the same direction also, connect them together.

Todhunter stopped for tea with Dobson and returned home after dark. On his way home he followed almost exactly the route he believed Beth would most likely have taken, and every now and then he whistled in the hope that if she was in trouble, she would let him know where she was by barking ; but it was a slender hope, for he had never heard her bark since the time when she stopped out in the great blizzard.

A little before midnight Todhunter, who had, of course, not been to bed the previous night, walked up to his farm utterly weary and dejected, but as he rounded the corner of the byre he saw Beth lying at the entrance to the sheepfold and the five sheep in the fold beyond her. In a moment all his weariness was forgotten and he was so pleased to see her all right that he came very near to making a fuss of her, a thing he never did with any of his dogs.

*   *   *   *   *

When Beth had been left the night before to take the five ewes home she had found almost at once that one of them was soft and unable to travel except very slowly. The ewe had been worried by maggots which had pulled her down a great deal and she had not yet fully recovered ; but Todhunter, in the dark, had not noticed it or else he would never have asked Beth to drive it home.

Beth knew very well that if she attempted to force the soft ewe it would almost certainly give up altogether, and probably lie down and thus make it impossible for her to drive it at all. Beth never thought of leaving it behind, but patiently coaxed it along, keeping well off when it showed signs of giving up, and endeavouring to quietly hustle it when it went on with the others. It was a beautiful exhibition of a really high-class dog driving sheep, had there been anyone there to see it, but for all that it was slow work ; and daylight found Beth still painstakingly driving the five ewes at the very best pace that the soft one could possibly go, and still some way from home.

As Beth crossed a piece of very much cut-up ground on Burton's fell she came over a low ridge to find herself within a hundred and fifty yards of Burton, who was walking across her front accompanied by two dogs. Beth had not heard him walking on the springy fell grass, nor had any chance to get his wind, for she was going downwind herself. She saw him as soon as she topped the rise, and in a moment, without being seen, had dropped back out of sight.

Burton saw the sheep, very evidently being driven, and expecting to see their shepherd, or, at any rate, a dog, was surprised when they presently stopped and started to feed, but he did not then bother to investigate. He sent out his own dogs to gather his sheep and Edwards' sheep began to drift back the way they had come, but as soon as they topped the rise Beth met them, for she had no intention of having all her night's driving to do over again. The sheep turned back and went on grazing except the soft one, which lay down for a much-needed rest. It was impossible for Beth to go on as

long as Burton remained shepherding before
her, so she lay down behind a rock where she
could watch both her own sheep and Burton.

Burton spent the whole morning amongst
his sheep, and at last took a dozen with him off
towards home. He passed within about three
hundred yards of Beth's sheep, and the sight
of them recalled his perplexity of the morning :
he sent one of his dogs to fetch them. That
was almost too much for poor Beth, but she knew
very well that whatever happened she must
not be seen, and with a great effort she lay still ;
but such was her anxiety that, although she had
scarcely shifted her position for more than
four hours, yet she began to pant as she saw
Burton's dog gathering her sheep.

The soft sheep would scarcely move for Burton's
dog, who was plain of his style and rough, and
he let it drop out and fetched the other four only
up to his master. Burton recognised Edwards'
marks but he did not want to be bothered with
the sheep, so, much to Beth's relief, he left them
and went on home.

The way was then clear for Beth, but she
made no attempt to go on. She had long
realised that the sheep-stealing journeys were

to be made as much as possible at night, and her coming suddenly upon Burton seemed to her proof that they must be carried out entirely by night ; perhaps, too, she was afraid of meeting anyone else, at any rate she waited for dark. She slept most of the afternoon, waking every now and then and having a look to see that her sheep did not wander far : once or twice she got up and quietly showed herself before them when she thought that they were straying too far, but on the whole the sheep after the night's walk were ready to stay where they were, and were easily discouraged by meeting Beth every time that they tried to wander off. While Beth was asleep Todhunter unconsciously passed within half a mile of her.

As soon as it was dark, Beth once more got hold of her sheep and drove them the rest of the way home as fast as the soft one could travel. She arrived at the fold some time before Todhunter returned from his search for her, and anxiously awaited his return. She was rather worried as to whether she had done the right thing in waiting for nightfall, and as Todhunter came up to her it was that anxiety which was uppermost in her mind ; so when Todhunter rubbed her ears with : " Good lass, Beth lass, Beth," she mistook his pleasure at finding her safe for approval of her waiting for nightfall.

After that she never drove another stolen sheep by daylight.

CHAPTER XV

THE SEARCH

On the Wednesday evening Burton sent one of his sons to Edwards with the news of the sheep that he had seen of his, and described one of them which was noticeable on account of having very forward horns. The next morning Edwards went to find his sheep but, naturally enough, could see nothing of them. He remembered the ewe with the forward horns and he searched carefully for her not only on Burton's fell, but on his own as well, and in doing so he missed for certain one of the other ewes that Todhunter and Beth had stolen, and thought that he missed a third one also.

Edwards went to see Burton to find out more exactly where the sheep had been seen ; and Burton described how he had thought at first that they were being driven. Edwards wondered if they could possibly have been stolen, and Burton then remembered that he had lately missed a few sheep which he thought ought to have been about.

The next day Burton and Edwards together gathered out the whole of the former's flock, partly in search of Edwards' missing ewes, and partly to see if Burton had really lost any, or if they had simply wandered a little away from their heath. Burton then missed for certain nine or ten of the sixteen that had been stolen, and he began seriously to suspect that they had, in fact, been stolen.

Edwards returned to Burton's farm for his dinner where they further discussed the matter, and Burton professed to suspect Todhunter; he had no grounds except the obvious one that Todhunter's was the next farm to his in the direction in which Edwards' sheep had been travelling, and that he personally disliked Todhunter. Edwards did not think that the evidence was sufficient, but he was always easily led by anyone and presently let Burton persuade him into going with him to look through Todhunter's sheep. Burton's eldest son went with them.

They did not call on Todhunter first but went straight across the Scarsdale Beck to the north of the Black Crags where there was some sort of a ford, and climbed up on to Hellaw. They had three dogs with them, one of Edwards' and two of Burton's, and they gathered out Todhunter's higher-fell flock and looked them over. They found none of their own sheep and indeed all of them very evidently bore Todhunter's own marks which showed no signs of having been tampered with or changed. Then they went around the eastern end of the Black Crags and started to gather out Todhunter's lower-fell sheep.

Todhunter almost daily cleared out any stolen sheep from the eastern end of the crags, and took them back to the western end where they could not possibly get out, and he had done so only that morning, so that the sheep which the Burtons and Edwards found at the eastern end were Todhunter's own.

While they had been on the top of Hellaw the Burtons and Edwards were out of sight of Todhunter's farm, but soon after they started on his lower-fell sheep, Todhunter saw them. He took his gun and went to see them off his farm : Beth went with him. The Burtons continued to look over his sheep in the most barefaced manner as he came up, but Edwards, who was beginning to feel rather ashamed of the whole business, kept rather apart.

On Todhunter asking what they were at, Burton said that they had had some sheep stolen, and that they were looking for them. Todhunter ordered them off his land, whereupon Burton simply sent one of his dogs to fetch some sheep from farther along the crags. Todhunter, now in a towering rage, pointed to the dog and said :

" Call that dog in."

Burton only laughed, but Beth, who seeing her master obviously upset was anxious to help, took the pointed arm and angry voice as a plain chance for her, and she raced away after Burton's dog. The dog, simply thinking that Beth was another dog sent to run with him, paid no attention to her. Beth, who was very fast, strode up to him like a borzoi on a wolf and struck behind the ear ; as she got a hold she checked, and Burton's dog, going at a fair speed over rough ground, when his head was suddenly pulled sideways and downwards, turned a complete somersault breaking Beth's hold, and went skidding along on his back. Before Beth could make in again Todhunter whistled his stop note, and Beth lay down at once. Burton's dog, though not badly bitten, was a good deal shaken and cowed, and avoiding Beth he came in to his master's heel.

Todhunter then announced that he would shoot if they did not all instantly leave his ground. His anger made his expression and eyes look even wilder than usual, and it seemed quite possible that he would really put his threat into execution. The Burtons were inclined to make a stand, but Edwards, who thought that the matter had already gone too far, persuaded them to come away. Burton as a parting shot announced that they would go and see the squire and certainly return to finish their search.

Todhunter saw them off the place in silence and even after they had crossed the beck, he sat on a stone nursing his gun and watching them ascend the opposite slope. While he was yet watching them, Ursula Stuart came round the corner of the Black Crags up the track, on one of her quite frequent visits to Todhunter. She was naturally very surprised to see him sitting on a rock with his gun, glowering across the beck at the retreating backs of the three others.

She asked him what on earth he was at, and Todhunter, still towering with rage, told her.

Ursula had, of course, heard nothing of any sheep-stealing and she was inclined to take Todhunter's part, not only because she thought the whole thing rather shady of the others, but also because she instinctively sided with what appeared to her to be the weaker party.

Todhunter presently cooled down and was as pleasant to her as his dour nature would allow. He gave her tea which included part of a fine salmon that Todhunter's otter had caught for him in the Scarsdale Beck. Ursula knew well enough where it had come from, though not how it had been obtained, but she made no comment ; indeed she was used, on her visits to Wancheate, to being provided with her own salmon or venison. After tea they went out on to the fell-breast and Todhunter ran Jess, and let Ursula try her hand with Meg, Jess would not run for anyone but him. He did not take Fly, for she had become very crippled ; nor Beth, for he did not want to call even Ursula's attention to her unnecessarily, nor get her into the habit of seeing people again, and indeed that afternoon was probably the first occasion that Beth had been seen by anyone since she had started on her stealing work.

Todhunter, though sour enough with people, could be very delightful with his dogs, and he liked the keen interest that Ursula had in them. He took great trouble to show her how they were worked and to get Meg to run for her, so that when Ursula finally returned to the Manor, she told her husband the story of the search of Todhunter's farm with a good deal of bias on Todhunter's side ; though Todhunter was far too simple to have thought of pleasing her with that object. Ian not unnaturally got Ursula's point of view, and when Burton and Edwards came to ask permission to search the farm, he was pretty short with them, and told them that if they made any attempt to do so he would certainly back Todhunter in an action for trespass.

At Benridding Market on the Monday, the alleged sheep-stealing was in everyone's mouth. Edwards, who was essentially fair-minded and who regretted the part that he had played, was at great pains to make it clear that they had seen at least three-quarters of Todhunter's flock, in his eagerness to be fair he probably exaggerated there, and that they were all clearly Todhunter's own sheep. The result was that a general impression prevailed that whoever might be the thief it almost certainly was not Todhunter. Burton was not greatly liked, for his sale of the hay to Todhunter was not his only sharp business, and little attention was paid to him.

Several farmers had missed a few sheep but thought little of it, they now, however, began to wonder ; and there was a general looking through of flocks, and as a result nearly everyone, who had had sheep stolen, found it out, though they mostly did not know the exact number that had been lost. There was now no doubt that sheep had been stolen, and Sir Ian Stuart, who owned nearly all the affected farms, called on Jackson, a patriarch who rented a big farm close to the Manor and shepherded on the extreme northern end of Hellaw : his and Todhunter's were the only sheep on Hellaw, the vast space between being kept for deer and grouse. Jackson had farmed the Manor Farm ever since his father had retired, who in his turn had taken it over from his father, and he was generally admitted to know more about sheep than anyone for miles around, and usually did free much of the work that should have been done, not nearly so well and at an exorbitant fee, by the nearest cow-leech.

Jackson had lost some sheep and Ian knew that what he said would go with all the other farmers. Jackson confessed to being sorely puzzled, not so much by the fact that stealing was being carried on, for he had known of one or two other cases, but by the manner of its execution. He had heard of a case where large numbers of sheep were stolen and driven right away from the district, such stealing was carried on usually entirely, but certainly partly, by thieves outside the district ; Jackson scarcely believed that the present one was such a case, for the thieves would have had far less difficulty in taking a lot of sheep from one or two farms than they must have had in taking a few from a lot of farms, besides which a big mob of sheep bearing a dozen or more different marks would attract attention, though he admitted that it would be possible in some measure to change the marks.

On the other hand it seemed to him that too many sheep had been taken for it to be a local thief ; sometimes a not too scrupulous farmer took a few fat wethers and butched them, and it was the right time of year for that, as the hill shepherds killed all the sheep they needed for the winter in the autumn when they were fat, and hung up their carcases to be cured by the smoke in the kitchen chimney, or sometimes stored them along with geese in barrels : but no one could reasonably consume, be his family never so big, the number of sheep that had recently been stolen from about Stonethwaite.

Jackson had also known of a case which, in fact, he had helped to investigate but which had been hushed up, where lambs were stolen. The farmer, whose name Jackson would not tell, had had an extraordinary number of twin lambs ; as fell sheep rarely have more than two or three per cent. twins this was peculiar and the more so as a large proportion of this particular farmer's twins were gimmers, the farmers about were unaccountably losing lambs and the matter was looked into.

The case had no great interest other than the wonderful skill shown by the farmer in mothering the stolen lambs on to his own ewes. This was necessary, as once done his own heath-going ewes would take the lambs on to their heath, and the lambs when speaned would stick to their adopted heath. It is no easy matter to mother a strange lamb on to a ewe even when she has lost her own lamb and the skin is available, but without the skin the task is a hundred times more difficult. It was, of course, necessary to take away the ewe's own lamb while the strange one was being mothered on and the thief adopted every known method such as hobbling the ewe or tying her up in a shed, forcibly suckling the lamb, and wetting the lamb with the foster mother's milk ; but he had had other dodges, such as making the ewe something more than half-tight on whisky and pouring whisky also over the lamb. Once the ewe had taken to the strange lamb her own lamb also was put back on her and the job was done.

After apologising for straying on to the subject of lambs Jackson said that he thought that the homing instinct of fell sheep was a bar to any local farmer stealing and keeping the sheep, as it would be a great risk to put them in the enclosed land all of which was near the farms and so usually near the roads. And he thought that little good could be done by searching through the farms ; if there was to be any hope at all, all the farmers who had lost sheep would have to take part in the search, for no one could recognise

anyone else's sheep ; many of the farmers would
not care to do that ; and, if it was a local man,
the thief would be bound to get to know and
could easily get rid of the sheep somehow even
if it came to butching them, though he would
most likely be able to hide them in some deep
gill where they would scarcely be found ; or
if the marks had not been changed, which was
by no means sure, he could always drive them
on to a neighbouring fell where if they were found
they would prove no one's guilt.

Most of all, he said, though he would know
many of his own sheep and the other farmers would
do the same, he would not be prepared to swear
to them in a court of law if the marks had been
changed, and even if any of the other shepherds
could be found to do so, he did not believe that
any judge would convict on that evidence alone.

It was hardly an encouraging interview, but
Ian was glad that there was no need for a general
search of the fell farms, for he thought that such
a search was a very muddy business. However,
he offered a reward of £50 to anyone producing
evidence leading to a conviction, and the police
were informed.

Meanwhile Todhunter continued to make

his raids on the neighbouring farms as often, or more often, than before. After Beth's behaviour when she had run into Burton on her way home with Edwards' sheep, for Todhunter was able now to guess pretty well what had happened, he had such confidence in her sagacity that he began to think it simply impossible for her to be caught. His only fear was that the stolen sheep be found on his farm, and that now seemed unlikely to happen ; besides all which in a fortnight or three weeks the buyer would come on his annual visit. Todhunter could then get rid of all his stolen sheep. He therefore set to work to get as many as he could before the buyer should come.

Beth, after the affair with Edwards' sheep, always took two nights if she found that she could not get them home before daylight. She would drive the sheep as far as she could before dawn, and then stop in the wildest convenient spot, lying up for the day somewhere handy where she could keep an eye on her sheep and yet be out of anyone's way ; if possible she hid in some nearby crags. Then at nightfall she would bring the sheep the rest of the way home. As soon as Todhunter found that, he took

much longer journeys after sheep, going sometimes as much as fifteen miles. That is, as he
would walk, for owing to the steep fell country
to go straight as the crow flies was impossible ;
if he did not go around the tops of the deep
dales or below the spurs of the fells he had to
go nearly as far climbing up and down the sides
and to do so would nearly always take longer,
so that he had to walk nearly twice as far on
an average as the distance would appear on a
map. He set off after dark and sent Beth
home with the sheep as early as possible, and then
went home himself as fast as he could by a
different way. He took care to get on to a road
or right of way by dawn, and finished his journey
in the daylight by road. If he met anyone he
had an excellent excuse for being so far from
home so early in the day, for he would say that
he had been out in the hope of catching the
thief, for £50 in those days was a little fortune
to a small fell farmer. Thus all the attempts
made to catch him only helped him in his stealing,
for Burton's ill-timed efforts to search his farm
had made a second and successful search most
unlikely.

CHAPTER XVI

THE DEVIL DOG

THE next light on the sheep-stealing, if light it could be called, was thrown by Tatters, the village cobbler at Stonethwaite. Tatters had had supper one night with a friend at Appleforth, a village about three miles from Stonethwaite across Ridderdale. He had a late and jovial evening but was sober enough when he started home about eleven o'clock at night.

Tatters' way lay through the Witches' Bog, a peat bog that was avoided by all and sundry if possible at night. At one time, as was clearly shown by the nature of the peat, it had been a birchwood ; and every now and then, probably by the action of the water, the peat would shift and throw up a branch of the long-buried birch. These branches glowed redly at night, and to anyone who did not know what they were, they strongly resembled the lighted windows of a distant cottage, and more than one stranger, benighted on the fell, had got into the bog in an attempt to reach one of these will-o'-the-wisps.

Although the night on which Tatters was crossing Ridderdale was fine, the sky was cloudy and the moon only occasionally appeared through rifts in the clouds. Tatters hurried along the narrow path that ran across one corner of the shallow end of the bog. He was a prey to superstitious fear, and glanced anxiously over his shoulder at a particularly bright and inviting will-o'-the-wisp, which glowed some little distance away to his right.

All at once Tatters heard something splashing through the wet bog and stopped, considerably frightened and nervous. The splashing came nearer and nearer and he was just considering head-long flight when he made out the grey forms of about half a dozen sheep. He was about to laugh at his fears and walk on when he bethought him that sheep would not walk close together across the bog in the middle of the night unless they were being driven. And he realised that here was a heaven-sent opportunity of earning the £50 reward as well as untold credit in the neighbourhood.

The sheep passed within twenty yards of Tatters but though their whitish wool, for they were Swaledales, showed dimly, he could see no one driving them, and the moon obstinately veiled her face. He was afraid that they would be gone, when at last the moon appeared, and Tatters saw Beth walking quietly along behind the sheep : at that moment she turned her head and looked in his direction and Tatters plainly saw her eyes gleaming in the dark. Tatters had plenty of time to see that there was no man in sight before the moon was gone again.

Probably Beth had never seen Tatters, for he had kept quite still, which will usually fool any animal, and the wind had blown across the path towards her, so that he had kept her wind throughout.

Tatters waited for some time in the certainty that the thief would come on after the dog, but as he began to realise that there was indeed no man he got frightened and set off home as quick as he could. By the time that he reached home he had quite made up his mind that what he had seen was a devil dog : he remembered that Beth had appeared coal black, for he had been looking at her slightly from behind where he could not see her white chest, and her white foot and the end of her tail were stained with bog water : he remembered the redly glowing eyes, and forgot that it would have been remarkable if her eyes had not glowed in the dark : Beth was a tallish bitch, but Tatters, affected by the eerie surroundings in which he had seen her and by his imagination, magnified her into a giantess. He reached home a thoroughly frightened man, convinced that the dog he had seen had not been of this world.

When Tatters told his wife, she told him plainly that he was drunk, still he had hardly expected anything else ; however, the next day he received no more credence from anyone else. Much annoyed at the doubts thrown on his sobriety, in the afternoon Tatters collected two of his cronies and they went out to the bog to find confirmation of his story in the soft peat mould.

Sure enough they found in several places the tracks of five or six sheep, and also the tracks of a dog which had evidently been following them, for though the dog's footprints were often laid on those of the sheep, the sheep's were nowhere on those of the dog. Tatters' foot-prints were plainly to be seen coming and going on the soft places in the path, but no other human tracks, except old ones on the path, were to be seen either on the path or in the peat. They could not trail the sheep except across the bog itself, for they made no marks on the sound fell.

After that there was no doubt expressed by anyone, not even his wife, but that Tatters' story was substantially true, although the footmarks did not support his story of a giant dog, and there was some difference of opinion as to whether a devil dog would have left any footprints at all.

Ursula Stuart, on hearing of the devil dog, was much interested and sought enlightenment from her oracle on all dog matters, going with unconscious irony to ask Todhunter. Her own idea was that it might have been some keen old dog amusing himself with sheep, for she had no faith in devil dogs. On arriving at Wan-cheate, Ursula thought that Todhunter looked bad and asked after his health. Todhunter, who had had some pain, replied :

" I'm nobbut verra feckless, thank the', m'Lady."

" Oh, I'm glad to hear that," but Ursula had guessed wrong for :

" Nay, m'Lady," said Todhunter, " I'm nobbut gay midlin'."

Ursula was none too certain even then, but as there seemed to be but two chances, she tried the other one :

" Oh, I'm sorry to hear that."

She then asked Todhunter for his explanation of the devil dog ; but he said that though some dogs might get working sheep on their own, adding that that was sometimes the start of worrying, no dog he believed would, to please himself, drive for long distances straight ahead, the dullest form of shepherding for the dog.   Ursula, suddenly seeing a possible explanation, asked :

" Could he be taught to do it ? "

For a moment Todhunter's face lit up as he replied :

" There's nowt in t'world that a good dog will ne come till, an he's taught aright, m'Lady."

" Do you mean a dog might be taught to steal sheep on his own ? "

But Todhunter realised that that was dangerous ground, the enthusiasm died out of his face and he only answered :

" Nowt's impossible ; we'ld best be awa'
te t'fell, m'Lady, an we're te run t'dogs afore
dark."

Ursula realised that Todhunter wished to
change the subject but put it down rather to his
usual moodiness than to any particular reason.

When that evening at dinner Ursula produced
the theory of an especially trained stealing dog,
she was well laughed at by Ian who said that
Todhunter was mad where his dogs were
concerned.

CHAPTER XVII

RESOLUTION

ONE night Todhunter took Beth to Calfhow Fell, which was about eleven miles from Wancheate and was shepherded by a farmer named Bennet : and he sent her off home with six two-shear wethers. Although the distance as Todhunter returned was but eleven miles, he knew that Beth would have to come sixteen or seventeen and he did not expect her till latish the second night. However, the wethers, all strong active Swaledales, would be able to come at a fair pace and he never doubted that they would make it all right in the two nights : indeed, he would never have taken her for sheep farther than those which she could comfortably bring in the second night.

But Beth never came that night and Todhunter knew that she would not come in the daytime. During the day he made a half-hearted

and unsuccessful attempt to look for her, more
to allay his anxiety than with any serious idea of
finding her, for he knew that he might easily
wander for a month over the fells and never
happen on to her.

*   *   *   *   *

It had taken Todhunter the greater part of
the night to get to Calfhow Fell, so that Beth had
not been able to start back before about three
o'clock in the morning. She drove her sheep
some six miles and then, as it began to get light,
she left them beneath some high crags, Wolf
Crags, so called as they were the scene of the
death of the last English wolf, and herself climbed
up into the crags to pass the day.

In the early afternoon Parker, the farmer on
whose fell she was, came past and saw Bennet's
sheep. He was not busy and, the stealing being
at that time in everyone's mind, he suspected that
the sheep, to be so far from home, for he happened
to know Bennet's marks, had probably been
stolen, and he thought the thief had perhaps been
frightened off and left them. Parker took the
six sheep along with him and drove them back
to Bennet's farm.

It was about all poor Beth could stand to see a strange man and dog drive her sheep away, but she dared not interfere, for she knew that she must not show herself. However, the idea never entered her single mind, even then, to go on home without the sheep, and she followed at a distance hoping for an opportunity to get hold of them once more. She was careful not to let Parker see her, which on account of the rough nature of the ground was easily avoided.

Parker drove the sheep into Bennet's intake, shut the gate on them, and went in and told Bennet what he had done. By then it was getting on for evening, and Bennet decided that they would be all right there for the night, and that he would look at them in the morning and see from what part of the fell they had come.

Beth lay up under a big stone on the fell just above the intake till dark, then she came down and set about recovering her sheep. There were a few other sheep in the intake but Beth had no difficulty whatever in picking out her own particular six wethers, which had kept fairly well together, and which she had kept her eye on, and she had no interest in the others. But she was faced with the wellnigh impossible task of getting them out of the intake : the gate was firmly shut and latched, as was the other gate leading to the farm, and the two hoggwalks each had their stones in place; Beth for all her cleverness had no idea of opening a gate, a thing even some cows can do. She had the trick, peculiar to sheepdogs, of leaping sideways through the bars ; she would race up to a gate and leap at the gap between two bars which she thought the widest, even though it were three feet or more off the ground ; if, as was almost always the case, the gap was not wide enough to let her deep chest through, she would give herself a twist in taking off and slip through on her side without touching the gate, landing as light as a feather on the far side ; and away with her without so much as breaking her stride.

Beth slowly and patiently drove her sheep the whole length of the fell wall and a little way down the side walls looking for a gap, but the wall was in good order and there was none : then she finished up once more against the fell wall. She still had no idea of going home without her sheep, and she made up her mind that, if she could jump the wall, the sheep could very well do it, too. The unfortunate sheep, however, had different

ideas, for the wall was nearly if not quite five feet
high and very nearly vertical.

All the coaxing in the world would not have
got the sheep over, nor did Beth try any, but
used force from the first.   It was a task that
scarcely one dog in a million could have achieved,
but Beth, whose great natural power had been
unusually increased by her peculiar work, was
probably the greatest forcing dog of all time,
and she had made up her mind that the sheep had
to go over, or through, or something.   She drove
in at the wretched sheep, snapping at their
quarters and, if one tried to bolt past her, she
met it in the face with raging eyes and flashing
jaws, till more than one of them had blood freely
running down its face.   Soon the sheep were in
a panic and would have tried to get over anything
to get away from the fiend that drove them.
One jumped at the wall, scrambled for a moment,
got his forefeet on top, hoicked himself up and
dropped down the other side.   Instantly two
more leapt at the same place, collided, lost their
feet, and fell heavily on their backs, but they were
up in a moment, for they were no fat south-
country brutes to get cast in a flat field.   After
a moment another sheep got over, and in doing

so dislodged the top stone. After that the other four got over without difficulty, other than that caused by their eagerness and trying to get over two or three at a time in the same place.

As soon as all six were over, Beth hopped over, caught hold of them, and drove them quietly along. There could be no greater proof of Beth's class than that once out on the fell her terrific force of a moment before dropped from her in an instant, and she drove the sheep as quietly as though they had just come without a hitch through an open gate.

Nothing tires sheep so much as being hurried at the beginning of a long drive, and so Beth's wethers, who had had a real blow at the wall, made slow time of it in spite of her best efforts, and dawn found her with six thoroughly beaten sheep still some five miles from home, but she was on the wildest part of the deer forest of Hellaw, where no one except Bellis or Patterson, the foresters, or possibly Moore, in search of a lost falcon, were likely to come. Beth would not drive on in the daylight but, leaving the sheep, she lay up for the day beneath an old stunted thorn tree, torn by the winds and twisted like a tup's horn. That day she saw no one, and at

235   *RESOLUTION*

dark drove the now rested sheep the last stage
to Wancheate : and great was Todhunter's joy
at seeing her come into the yard.

Poor Beth was pretty hungry, for she had had
no food for over two days and nights, and it was
Todhunter's first care to remedy that deficiency :
Beth as a rule was not a great doer, but that night
when she had finished, she looked as if she was
momentarily expecting a large family.

Todhunter did not lift many more sheep
after Bennet's six wethers, for he was expecting
the buyer and he had to allow a few days at least
that the altered ear marks might have more or
less healed. The wholesale buyer presently
came and took all the stolen sheep. Many had
been the different ear marks that had all been
changed somehow into Todhunter's own, and
so, though roughly his marks, they were all shapes
and sizes and some of them, if closely examined,
were scarcely healed. However, the buyer, who
as a result of the more or less general losses in
the great storm had great difficulty in getting
enough sheep, did not bother over the marks,
which he considered none of his business ; but
he gladly paid for the sheep, drove them away,
and butched them.

CHAPTER XVIII

TOO OFTEN TO THE WELL

AFTER the sale of his stolen sheep Todhunter was richer than he had ever been before, at least in actual cash, although his stock was still low, and indeed less than really belonged to the farm: he was relieved to get rid of his ill-gotten sheep and be free from the risk of discovery, and he made up his mind to give up his stealing, and to confine Beth once more to her legitimate work. But giving up was easier said than done, and the very sight of Beth was a continual temptation, for apart from the money he got by it, Todhunter had taken a very real pleasure in the performance of Beth, and in the opportunities that the work had given her to display her extraordinary sagacity and resolution.

Presently Todhunter began to break the tenth commandment in respect of some sheep belonging to a farmer named Mason, who shepherded at the south-western corner of Lake Southermere. Although Mason's marks, upper half near, swallow fork far, could be altered to Todhunter's high-fell marks fairly well by cutting off the lower half of the near ear and thus making it a crop, and by making an extra big fork in the far ear ; and his fell was an easy one to take sheep off, yet Todhunter had left his sheep alone for the very reason that he now coveted them : Mason had a very fine breed of Swaledales, they were inclined to be taller than most Swaledales, and their wool was whiter, in fact they were a distinct type, and almost any shepherd in the district, if he saw a dozen or more of them, would recognise them as " Mason's ewes," although a few of them might be little different from a few of other people's.

Todhunter had thought that the different type would make the stealing of any of Mason's sheep more dangerous, and so as he would have got little or no more money for them off the buyer, he had not thought it worth his while. However, his appreciation of sheep was second only to his appreciation of a good dog, though a very poor second, be it said, and he had long been anxious to get hold of some of Mason's breed, but Mason was very sticky about parting with any of his gimmer sheep. Todhunter at last decided to steal a few of Mason's ewes for his own use and chance the risk, but he waited till after the new year that the ewes might be with lamb to Mason's tups.

There was a heavyish fall of snow about Christmas, which, however, did not freeze on top and so did little harm to the sheep who could dig for their food, yet it lay on the high fells till after the middle of February. The snow, as long as it lay, made it impossible for Todhunter to take any of Mason's sheep, for the footmarks would have been plain for anyone to read. It was not till the first week in March that Todhunter and Beth took eight of the best ewes that Todhunter could find in the dark on Mason's fell ; Beth brought them easily in the same night, for it was not far from Mason's to Wancheate. The whole thing went off without a hitch, and Todhunter changed the marks and drove the sheep up into the crags.

From the very first Todhunter had difficulty with one of the nicest of the ewes, she was a fine tall ewe of the real Mason type, but she was the worst wratch that Todhunter had ever seen :

she continually came down from the crags and easily jumped over any of the walls of his enclosures in her efforts to return to her heath ; but the Scarsdale Beck or the lake stopped her, and as often as Todhunter found her down by the waterside, he drove her back into the crags with the others. She was such a nuisance that Todhunter several times came near to getting finished with her by knocking her on the head, but she was such a fine ewe that he did not like to do that, and he thought that probably once she had lambed she would settle down pretty well.

Todhunter had no idea exactly when Mason had loosed his tups, and he did not know that his wild ewe had jumped out of the field, into which she and a lot more had been put while the tups were loosed, and had returned to the fell ; so she had not taken the tup till all the ewes had been returned to the fell when, as was the general practice, one or two tups were turned loose on the fell for a little to catch any ewes that might have missed. The result was that the wild ewe was not due to lamb till several weeks after the others.

Fell sheep, being but little domesticated, have

often strong primitive instincts, and Todhunter's wild Mason ewe had especially so. As she approached lambing and felt herself in trouble her uneasiness drove her more than ever to try to get back to the country that she knew. Todhunter kept her in a pasture amongst the other ewes that had already lambed and kept an eye on her ; but at the very time when he expected her to lamb at any moment, she suddenly disappeared altogether. Todhunter felt sure that she would not have crossed the beck and supposed that she had gone up into the crags to be by herself. He was pretty busy, as was usual in lambing time, and did not feel like making an extensive search, which would very likely prove unsuccessful, for the ewe would take care not to be seen, and could easily dodge him in the crags, and might even be missed by a dog ; or even if she was found, if she had lambed she might refuse to move for a dog, although he knew that Beth could shift almost anything. Such a wild kind of ewe would fight like a tigress in defence of her lamb, and it was unlikely that the lamb would fall a prey to a fox or other powerful vermin. And so Todhunter decided to let her take her chance and lamb by herself.

In fact, the ewe had gone home. There was not a great deal of water in the Scarsdale Beck, and she had found a place where, by jumping from stone to stone, she had only been in deep water the last few feet. She did not go back to Mason's farm, but on to the high fell to her own heath ; there she lambed and for some days escaped notice. However the lamb's wool, everywhere very white except for his black legs and face, showed up very plainly, far plainer than the old ewe's rather greyish wool, and one of Mason's sons, seeing the young lamb, thought that they would be safer in one of the fields, and went to fetch the ewe and lamb in.

When young Mason saw Todhunter's wool marks he was considerably surprised, but when he got near he was sure that, not only was it one of his father's ewes, but that he recognised her individually, for her determined wratching had caused him a deal of trouble at one time and another and he knew her only too well. He fetched them both down to one of the fields near the farm, and brought his father to look at them. Old Mason also recognised the ewe, and a close inspection of her ears showed that the marks had been made or altered fairly recently, and certainly since she was a lamb ; and there were signs where the old wool mark had been plucked off.

If any further proof were necessary, Mason had a third mark, not to distinguish his sheep from other people's, but to distinguish one family from another of his own breed : this mark took the form of tiny snicks on the horns, the snicks being in different places or in different numbers according to which family the ewe belonged to. This ewe, and indeed all that Todhunter had taken, for he had taken all from the same part of the fell and they were of the same family, had only one small snick on the underside of the near horn : the snicks had been made as hoggs, and had become faint so that Todhunter, who knew nothing of them, had overlooked them.

Mason thought that he had sufficient proof that the ewe was his : both he and his son recognised her, there was the horn mark, and any of the neighbouring shepherds would bear witness that she appeared to be his type of ewe, all that might not bear much weight in a court of law, but most important of all, one of Todhunter's own ewes could have no possible inducement to leave her own heath and cross the Scarsdale

Beck and several miles of rough country to get to Mason's fell.

Before taking any steps Mason went and saw Jackson who, he knew, would give him sound advice. Jackson agreed, not only that there was conclusive proof to him that Todhunter had stolen the ewe, but that a court also would probably convict. Mason then applied to the police and a warrant was obtained for Todhunter's arrest.

CHAPTER XIX

IN THE NARROW WAY

THE next afternoon a police sergeant, the constable from Stonethwaite, one Peters by name,
and Mason and one of his sons went out to
Wancheate Farm. Mason and his son went,
for Mason believed that he would find some
more of his ewes there : he had missed some of the
eight which had been stolen, but as the stealing
scare had died down, he at the time had been
ready to believe that they had perhaps been
buried in a snowdrift in some deep gill, or had
fallen a prey to any of the natural accidents to
which fell sheep are liable, especially in the
winter.

When the Masons and the police drove up
in Mason's trap along the rough track from Stonethwaite, Todhunter was in the yard with Beth ;
the old otter, who with age had grown fat and
lazy and now did little to earn his keep, was

sunning himself under the byre wall : the other three dogs were shut in the kitchen. As the trap drove up, Beth and the otter melted away like shadows, and the otter was never seen again by anyone : no doubt, when put to it, he was well able to get his own living in the becks round about.

The sergeant proceeded to charge Todhunter with sheep-stealing in full legal jargon. Todhunter said little other than to tell him not to talk rot, but when Mason told him about the returned ewe he began to realise that things looked very black against him. The sergeant said that Todhunter would have to go to the police station, but he objected on the grounds that he had three dogs in the kitchen and four cows in milk and that if he was taken off there would be no one to attend to them : the sergeant said that he would see to that, and told Peters to start off with Todhunter to Stonethwaite on foot, as there would be no room for all five of them in the dogcart, as all except Todhunter were big men and the cart was small.

Peters had no fear of losing Todhunter on the way, for he was a head taller and nearly twice as heavy, and he was a particularly good runner, indeed he had won fell races at local sports. They did not think it necessary to make Todhunter walk four miles with his hands tied, and the local constabulary boasted no handcuffs in working order. Peters and Todhunter therefore set off at once, while the others stopped to search the farm for any signs of Todhunter's guilt, and the fell for any more of Mason's sheep.

As soon as Peters and Todhunter started, Beth followed them, keeping as near as she could and yet out of sight. She guessed from Todhunter's manner that something serious was up, and she kept running on past them, and lying down in a good place near to the track, where she could not be seen by Peters, and yet could get a good look at Todhunter to see if she could make out what was going on. As time went on she became more and more worried, and more certain that Todhunter was in trouble and that she should try to do something to help.

Beth finally took up her position right by the track behind one of the mongrel trees to wait for Peters and Todhunter to come up ; the mongrel trees were three pollard ashes that grew by the side of the track about half-way between Stonethwaite and Wancheate Farm : in one of them, where the bump had been made by the pruning, a rowan tree grew as big round as a man's thigh, and also a sycamore scarcely less big, as well as several healthy shoots of the ash itself. These parasite trees must have been sown many years before by birds in the cracks of the pollard ash, but they apparently had no roots, getting their nourishment direct from the ash tree itself, and they had so well grown into the tree that it was very difficult to see exactly where the ash finished and the rowan and sycamore started. The effect in summer when the tree bore all three different kinds of leaves at the same time was most extraordinary. That was the most remarkable of the three trees but one of the others supported a small thorn tree and the third a small sycamore, but the thorn did not grow so well into the ash as the rowan and sycamore did. The mongrel trees grew close to the beckside at a point where the side of Hellaw sloped steeply almost down to the beck, and there was barely more than enough room for the track itself. Beth could scarcely then have asked for a better place for an ambush.

As Peters and Todhunter came up Beth, her ears flat on her skull, peered cautiously over a

jutting root. Peters was far too unobservant to
notice her, and Todhunter was too depressed
to take much notice of anything. Beth became
absolutely certain that something was very very
wrong, and just as they came up to the tree, she
slipped from behind it and lay down in their path,
her eyes on Todhunter's face.

Peters, considerably startled, pulled up short,
saying :

" Gawks on ! yon's Tatters' divil dog."

Todhunter realised that his chances, already
pretty slim, were made the thinner by Beth's
well-meant but untimely appearance and, deciding
to try a last faint hope, he said in an urgent
tone that there was no mistaking :

" Beth, here Beth ; Beth, here Beth."

Beth got up at once, but did not move and
obviously did not understand what he wanted ;
Todhunter thereupon lurched heavily against
Peters, who instinctively grabbed at him. Beth,
thinking that Todhunter was being attacked,
instantly understood his commands, took two
strides, and leapt, a black flash, straight at Peters'
face. Peters threw up an arm just in time, as
Beth landed with her forefeet on his chest with such
force as to make him stagger back : her teeth

closed over his forearm, ripping his uniform, and laying his arm open to the bone.

The next moment Beth was away and lying flat on her belly two paces off, trying to watch both Peters, and Todhunter who at once started off up the fellside : Beth was about to follow him when Peters unwisely did the same ; he had not taken a stride before his calf was laid open, and he turned to see Beth lying facing him, her ears back, her eyes slitted narrow, and her wicked jaws open. Peters was no coward, but Beth was not a sight to inspire confidence, and he had not even a stick. He backed away from her till he was off the track and amongst the stones by the side, then he stooped down to pick up a big one, but as his fingers closed over it he was aware that Beth was upon him. Peters straightened up with a jerk, but not before Beth had cut his shoulder, and was once more back in her old position, lying facing him two paces away. He tried again for his stone, crouching very carefully and never taking his eyes off Beth ; he felt for a big one and straightened up once more, then he hurled the stone at Beth with all his might, but she saw it in his eye and the movement of his arm and dodged it with contemptuous ease.

Peters then walked straight towards Beth, but she got up and backed away : he suddenly rushed in, in the hope of getting in a kick, but Beth whipped out sideways, and her wicked teeth met for an instant in Peters' leg ere she was once more lying watching him. Peters made one more effort to go after Todhunter, but saw, out of the corner of his eye, Beth begin her rush, and he turned only in the very nick of time to avoid another cut.

Peters had to admit that he was thoroughly defeated : Beth was far too quick to let him do her any damage, and she made it impossible for him to move away. He looked cautiously over his shoulder and saw Todhunter climbing steadily up the fellside, but Peters could do nothing but wait till the others came along in the trap to his assistance, or until Beth cleared off and left him.

Todhunter did not exert himself unduly going up the fellside, but after fifteen minutes or so he reached the crest, once beyond which he would no longer be able to see the track. He stood for a moment silhouetted against the sky, while he looked down at the two on the track still motionless eyeing each other like two tom cats, each waiting for the other to give an opportunity for a rush. Then his voice came faintly :

" That'll do, Beth, Beth, that'll do."

Beth sprang up and, without even glancing at Peters she raced by him and started up the fellside : the next moment Todhunter disappeared over the crest. Peters started to go after them, but his right leg had been badly bitten twice and, while he had been standing still on it for the best part of a quarter of an hour, it had grown stiff : he realised that, with the long start Todhunter had, pursuit was hopeless, and he limped back the way he had come towards Wancheate to report his prisoner's escape to his superior officer ; and well he knew what the latter would have to say about it. Indeed Peters was glad that he had honourable scars of battle to show, and he hoped that they would be counted to him in some measure for credit.

CHAPTER XX

FLY

BEFORE Peters reached Wancheate, he met the trap coming towards him with the Masons, and the sergeant, the Masons' dog brought to help them to look for any more stolen sheep, and Meg, Fly, and Jess, each with a strong cord attached, sitting dejectedly under the seat. The sergeants' remarks on hearing of Todhunter's escape exceeded even the best form which Peters had known him show, but unfortunately are unrepeatable.

As they came into Stonethwaite they stopped while arrangements were made for a boy to go out and milk Todhunter's cows till they could be removed. Peters got out at his cottage taking the three dogs with him and, as the sergeant's sarcastic query whether he thought that he could keep even them safely was still burning his ears, he tied them up securely in his woodshed.

As soon as she was tied up Fly lay down grey-hound fashion, her hind feet drawn up under her, her quarters standing up on each side of her back, and her grizzled muzzle stretched out along her forepaws : once in that position she never moved but, with her dim old eyes un-blinking, she continued to stare straight into the opposite wall, seeing only she knew what beyond the whitewashed bricks.

Peters brought them some food and water, securely fastened the door, there was no window, and left them. In the course of the night Meg and Jess drank a little, and Meg ate a little ; but Fly never moved.

Jess spent most of the night on her haunches howling dismally : Meg chewed through her rope and made the round of the shed in an unsuccessful attempt to get out.

Fly never moved.

In the morning when Peters came he narrowly secured Meg in her attempt to whip through the opened door. Then he led her and Jess out for a little run : he brought them back, tied them up, and undid Fly's string : Fly was lying as he had left her, still staring with dim eyes into the opposite wall. Peters twitched the string gently with a "Come on, gal," but, as she did not move, he pulled it more sharply. She fell over on to her side.

Fly was dead.

Later in the day Jackson, on Sir Ian Stuart's instigation, took over Meg and Jess. Ursula was anxious to have Meg, Jess had never run for her, but she gave up the idea as she thought that Meg would be wasted since she had no sheep to work her on.

Jackson had some trouble at first, for both Meg and Jess were for ever slipping away back to Wancheate, a distance of only four miles, however he knew where to go and look for them, and as they always found it deserted they soon gave up and stuck to the Manor Farm well enough.

After a little Meg ran fairly well for Jackson, but it was some time before Jess would do any work for him ; however, she had taken more after Bright than Fly, and Jackson was a good hand, so she presently came to all right. Ursula, who saw them both work, believed that they were never either of them as good as they had been when running for Todhunter.

CHAPTER XXI

TRIAL BY WATER

AFTER his escape Todhunter hung about the top of the fell till he saw the trap go by with the police and both Masons : then he went home by way of the Crag Gate, and collected some food and what money he had in the house, and it was a fair sum for he did not understand or believe in banking. He went back on to the top of Hellaw and lay up till dark.

As soon as it was dark, Todhunter set off once more. He went out of his way to avoid villages and houses, but he held generally north-east till he should have got around the Solway Firth, for his aim was the Scottish Highlands and possibly the Western Isles : Ursula Stuart had talked to him sometimes of the land whence she had come and it sounded the kind of refuge that he sought. He travelled pretty fast for he was not afraid of running into anyone without receiving warning from Beth, who knew well enough that Todhunter's night journeys were strictly private, besides Todhunter knew that one man could not stop him without a gun, for his escape from Peters had shown him that in Beth he had an unjointed armour, at least against one man and possibly more.

Dawn found Todhunter within a mile or two of the border and he lay up in a thick wood called the Oak Crop : the origin of the name was that at one time the land on which the wood grew had belonged to a small holder and was the only break in the big estate of the local squire. The squire tried hard to buy it but the owner would not sell ; however, he finally agreed to let it at a huge rent to the squire for one crop, supposing, of course, that he intended to sow corn of some sort, but the old squire sowed it with acorns, and the crop of oak trees was not ready to cut for nearly a hundred years. Long before then the land was useless for almost anything and the lessor's son gladly sold it for a fair price to the squire's son before the trees were half-grown. The crop was never reaped, and Todhunter found the thick wood an excellent refuge in which to pass the day.

Once across the border Todhunter travelled in a north-westerly direction, and after the second night he went by day for he felt that he was reasonably safe from pursuit : the fastest means of travel were the horse and the mail coach, and no description of him could have been circulated by other means than these, for carrier pigeons, which were the only telegraph, had to be sent first of all by coach before they could be loosed to carry a message back whence they had come, so they would be of no use to the police in his case. Still he avoided roads and villages as much as possible.

On the afternoon of the fifth day of his journey Todhunter came to the River Sturn, it was running strong and swift and he walked upstream looking for a bridge. After a mile or more, and just after passing a village which he avoided, he came to a pool known locally as the Devil's Cauldron : it was a magnificent sight, at once beautiful and awful ; the water came into the pool at the top side, not in a fall, but in a race through which the water ran deep and very swift in one smooth rush. The water from the race, as it came slanting into the deep pool of the Devil's Cauldron, drove in an unbroken current right beneath the surface of the pool, so that the pool was a raging, eddying vortex and well earned its name.

As Todhunter came to the pool it was indescribably beautiful: the afternoon sun shone into the face of the race and made a tiny rainbow in the spray above the spot where the race entered the pool, the water both in the race and in the pool was shot with every shade of greens and blues, and in the cracks of the rocks around those most lovely trees birches and rowans grew thickly, and as there had been rain in the morning the air was heavy with the scent of birch trees after summer rain.

The river flowed broad and smooth above, but gradually narrowed into the race, and where it narrowed Todhunter found his sought-for bridge. It was a footbridge that should have spanned the river nearly a quarter of a mile upstream, but nearly every winter the floods broke it loose from its moorings and carried it downstream, to be taken up once more in the summer when the water had subsided. It had not yet been moved, and lay jammed skewways across the river between two boulders ; it lay tilted over at an angle of nearly forty degrees, and was still slippery from its long immersion in the winter floods.

Todhunter had not spent half of his life shepherding in the Black Crags above Wancheate Farm to be afraid to cross a river on a tilted bridge, be the river never so swift, and he climbed down over the rocks and started carefully across the narrow bridge, keeping his balance by means of the single handrail, which except for a gap in the middle served for most of the way. When he came to the break in the handrail, he stopped for a moment to consider how he should negotiate the gap.

Beth, who was following her master close and carefully looking where she put her feet on the slippery bridge, did not see him stop till she all but ran into his legs. As she tried to stop in a hurry she missed her feet and slipped : for a moment she clung with her forefeet, but the water dragged at her hindquarters and bushy tail and pulled her down. Beth made no sound, but Todhunter saw her out of the corner of his eye, he suddenly remembered the frightful pool below, and in a flash, without stopping to think, he shouted " Beth " and leapt out into the water towards her.

Once in the water Todhunter was held power-less, and the pair of them went down into the race within a yard of each other, but with no more control over their movements than two straws. As they came into the steep race they went faster and faster, and finally were dashed from view beneath the waters of the Devil's Cauldron.

For nearly half a minute there was no sign of man or dog, and the first to show was Beth ; she came to the surface near the lower end and drifted down out of the pool. She was carried this way and that in the eddies, and finally, fifty yards downstream, she stuck on a flat shingly bank : the river seemed to hesitate whether it would leave her on the bank or carry her off down-stream, then an extra strong eddy gave her a bit of a push, and she stuck fairly firmly, her head and shoulders on the pebbles and her quarters still lying in the shallow water, with her long coat rising and falling in the stream like seaweed.

Presently Todhunter appeared face downwards floating downstream. He turned for a moment half on to his left side and the whole of his right temple showed smashed in against some sub-merged rock. The body hesitated for a second against the bank where Beth lay, and then was carried off downstream to be seen and taken out in the village which Todhunter had passed on his way up. John Todhunter had gone, with straightened back, to the Green Fields where Fly, no longer lame, was waiting to meet him at the Gate.

CHAPTER XXII

LOYAL HEART

MEANWHILE Beth lay still, half in and half out
of the water, as quiet as the body of her master.
A passing raven dropped out of the sky and settled
on a nearby rock ; he looked long and closely
at Beth, his head first on one side and then on
the other : he saw that her flanks heaved, though
ever so gently, and he settled down to wait till
the spark of life should die, patiently preening
himself the while. The raven is particular about
his meals, he likes them really high and well-
seasoned if possible ; but anyway, unless driven
by real hunger, he will not start till life has quite
gone ; unlike the carrion crow, that cruel devil
that will attack the eyes and tongue of cast and
helpless sheep. However, the raven reaps the
reward of his virtue for he is left unmolested by
the hill shepherds, while they persecute his
smaller cousins whenever possible.

The raven preened away for more than an hour, till he could find no fault with even the least of his feathers, but still Beth made no move, only her flanks yet heaved very gently. The raven settled his heavy head into his wide shoulders and became as motionless as his intended meal, only his black eye gleamed watchfully. Finally Beth choked and staggered uncertainly to her feet, but almost immediately lay down again. She stared anxiously about for Todhunter and then, getting up once more, she moved away unsteadily upstream, while the disappointed raven flew away in search of other food.

Beth cast upstream past the head of the race, and then down again below the bank where she had been washed up, then she swam to the other side : it was easy to see then how near she had been to drowning and how weak she yet was, for she was carried some little distance downstream before she was able to make the far bank. She cast upstream once more beyond the race, and then for the first time she became really conscious that she was lost.

There is nothing in the world so pitiful as a lost dog, no other animal knows the same despair, and Beth, for the first time in her life, really lost

her head. She was not made of the stuff that
sits down and howls, but her frantic, hopeless
search was, if anything, more pathetic. She
cast madly up and down the banks of the river,
ran round the neighbouring country in small
circles, and swam and reswam the river half
a dozen times. Finally, long after dark, and when
she was utterly exhausted, Beth lay down near the
broken bridge and slept ; she slept but fitfully
and woke often, but she made no move till daylight.

During the night Beth recovered her wits.
She realised that her master was nowhere about,
and she did the only thing she knew, started
off to go the eighty or a hundred miles home.
She knew the way perfectly well and went steadily
along. In the early morning of the second day
she heard a rabbit screaming and on investigation
found it in a snare. It was a very welcome find,
for Beth, who had had nothing to eat since the
evening before she was lost, was beginning to
feel the effects of real hunger, and she had been
too shy to go scrounging for food in the villages.
She soon polished off the rabbit and, feeling
comfortable and well fed, curled herself up for
a nap. She awoke strengthened and more

determined than ever to get home as soon as possible.

The late afternoon of the third day after Todhunter's death found Beth travelling southwards over Hellaw. She had come thirty miles since dawn, although not in a straight line, for she had gone out of her way to avoid towns and villages and to keep to the wildest parts of the country. She was tired and footsore, for her feet had been cut by the sharp screes, but as she came across Hellaw, on the ground she knew so well, she quickened her pace, and went down through Crag Gate and over the lower fell-breast as though she had only just started.

Beth, although she had come home in half the time that it had taken Todhunter and her to go out, felt absolutely sure that she would find Todhunter waiting at the farm, and it was this certainty of seeing her master once more that spurred her on over the last two or three miles.

Poor Beth ! as she came around the corner of the byre across the yard and up to the kitchen door, she knew with deadly certainty that Todhunter had not been there for several days : the whole place smelt cold and deserted and the

Todhunter smell had almost gone. The door was shut, and as Beth went and lay down along the sill, she suddenly felt very, very tired. She lay across the doorway till dark, then she got stiffly up and went over to drink from the yard trough, but, finding it stagnant and foul, she went out and drank from the Wancheate Gill where it ran close by the farm. She returned to the kitchen doorway and slept across the sill.

The next morning, when Beth got up and stretched herself, she was very stiff, for her muscles ached after her long, hard travelling and they were the worse for the frightful buffeting she had received in the water of the Devil's Cauldron ; and besides, she was really hungry, for the meal she had had from her rabbit had long since died in her. Worse than her physical discomfort, or perhaps partly because of it, was her loneliness : the very certainty that she had the day before felt of finding her master at Wancheate, now that it had been disappointed, made her the less hopeful of his return. There was nowhere, however, that she could go and look for him : she had nothing to do but wait. But above her weariness and hunger, above her loneliness, above

all else there flamed her loyalty like a shining
sword.

Beth was not made of the stuff that would
lie quietly down and wait in the hope of her
master's return : in the meantime she must
do something, do something for him, and she
set out to do the only thing she knew, gather
his sheep. On the previous afternoon as she
came across Hellaw, through the Crag Gate,
and down over the lower fell-breast, Beth had
been thinking only of Todhunter, and not
bothering about sheep, else she would have
noticed that there were no sheep, where always
before since she could remember sheep had
fed.

All the sheep had been removed, even the
cattle had gone, and Todhunter's fell pony, and
the very pigs that fed on the skim milk, all had
gone : on all Wancheate Farm there was not a
single living thing, save the wild creatures,
Beth, and an old brindled tom cat, who, though
he had been caught and taken away with the rest
and though he cared little for Todhunter, yet
was attached to his home, and had returned to
live as best he could on the grouse, and now and
then a young leveret, or rabbit, or anything else

that he could catch. He was much better off than Beth, he had always been a poaching old devil, and he understood how to get his own living, which Beth did not. Besides, the cat was not upset by the loss of his master, as Beth was, and as long as he could get enough to eat and sleep in the bracken, where it was stored for bedding in an open shed, he was happy.

Beth found the old tom in his bracken with the remains of a grouse that he had killed and almost entirely eaten. As Beth appeared he arched his back and spat, but Beth was not to be bluffed, and most of a cat's armoury is bluff, for she was all but starving, and she drove him off it and finished off the grouse, bones, feathers and all.

Many dogs will work sheep for their own amusement, but that alone could scarcely account for Beth's next action : sheep-stealing may have been Beth's favourite work, indeed with the possible exception of deer-poaching it probably was, but she also thought that it was the work which pleased Todhunter most, for she knew well that it was the most difficult that he had ever asked her to do, and that he was always anxious while it was going on : perhaps, too, she had some dim idea that the farm should be stocked against his return. Whatever her idea, Beth set out at dark, as she had so often done before under his guidance, to steal sheep for her master. She waited for dark, naturally enough, for all her stealing work had been done at night : then she set off across the Scarsdale Beck, up Blenthorpe, and over the Great Rigg.

*　　*　　*　　*　　*

Burton had only a few days before turned out his ewes and lambs on to the fell ; and a grand sight it was as, on a fine evening, Burton drove nearly a thousand sheep, hoggs and shearlings as well as ewes, out on to the fell bottom ; once on the fell he ceased driving and let them go on their own. They belonged to three different heaths, and they at once divided up into the three lots and went stringing away towards their own heaths. Each lot was led by an old bell wether, who wore the bell fastened to his neck by a steel spring hoop, that could be pulled open to admit his neck and then sprang together again : each bell had a different note, and all had a lovely tone, and could be heard for an immense distance. It was thought that the sheep knew the note of their own particular wether's bell and would follow it, although now the bells are no longer in use, the shepherds relying on the heath instinct of their sheep. Besides the notes of the three bells was the pleasant calling of the anxious old ewes to their lambs, who, however, paid little attention to their mothers, but ran and played about amongst themselves, till they thought that they were lost, when they called plaintively and raced after their mothers. Each flock strung out till it was nearly half a mile long as the sheep slowly wended their several ways to their respective heaths.

Beth found on the heath, on the top of Blenthorpe nearest the Great Rigg, nearly three hundred sheep of all ages, as well as over one hundred lambs running at the sides of their dams. She painstakingly gathered up every one she could see and drove them down over the Great Rigg and down the screes towards the Scarsdale Beck. She had driven many a lot of stolen sheep over the Rigg and down the screes since that first night when Todhunter and she stole their first lot from Burton, for all the sheep that she had brought to Wancheate had had either to come that way or from the opposite direction down Crag Gate, and far the most had come by way of the screes and across the beck.   So that she now well knew the best way off the Great Rigg and down the screes.

Beth had no very great difficulty in driving her sheep down the screes, the ewes who had lambs were a bit tiresome and held things up ; and wherever there was a narrowish pass the big mob of sheep were inclined to jam so that the work was slow, but for all that they kept moving pretty steadily down and all went as well as could reasonably be expected.   But when they came to the beck it was a very different matter : it was one thing to drive three or four sheep across the Scarsdale Beck, but a very different thing to try to drive as many hundreds, and many of them ewes with lambs, the most difficult of all sheep to force.   Indeed, had they been young lambs, it would probably have been quite impossible, but they were getting fairly strong, and their mothers did not worry so much about them as they had done a few weeks before.

Beth brought the mob of sheep to her usual crossing-place, and began the herculean task of getting them over.   She unconsciously did the best thing possible, for as the young sheep and geld ewes were the most active, they were the more determined in their efforts to break away, and Beth was forced to pay most attention to them, and not bother so much with the ewes and lambs, who gave little trouble when left alone, but who would have been almost impossible to force first into the water. The great number made her task the more difficult, but Beth was here, there, and everywhere, like a mad thing, and many were the sheep that bore the marks of her teeth, though not seriously. At last some of the geld sheep began to cross, and Beth followed up her advantage hard and now forced the old ewes and lambs in with the rest. The ewes began to go in and some of the lambs followed them, some of their own free will, and some knocked in, in the general mêlée, but some stood ba-a-a-ing on the bank, and there were more than a few that Beth shouldered bodily in, tumbling them into the water head over heels. Once in the water there was no getting out on the same side as they went in, for Beth was there to meet them in the face and drive them back.

For an hour Beth worked desperately on the

bank, and in that hour she did more work than she had done in many a hard day's shepherding on the fell : but, at the end of that hectic hour, there was no sheep left on the Blenthorpe bank of the beck.   Beth, like the captain of a sinking ship, was the last to leave the bank and swim across ; there she found five ewes, whose lambs had been drowned, blaring hopelessly on the Wancheate Bank.   Beth gathered up all the sheep, some of whom had wandered a little away, and the five childless ewes with them, and drove them up towards the farm.   She had some difficulty with the ewes that had lost their lambs, but they were the more willing to come, because many of the ewes had more or less mislaid their lambs in the turmoil, and in the general calling of ewes and lambs they could not be sure that they might not find their own lambs.

Luckily for Beth, all the gates in her path had been left open when the farm had been cleared of stock, but she did not drive her sheep into the small fold in the yard, as she had usually done with other sheep, perhaps she realised that they could not all get in anyway, or more likely, because Todhunter was not there she decided to drive them up into the crags, which had always been the final destination of the stolen sheep, after their marks had been altered in the fold.

Many of the sheep were weary after the trouble at the beck and the ewes and lambs kept stopping and looking for each other, so they moved but slowly, and it was beginning to get light as they came up into the crags. There Beth left them, and herself, after climbing higher still into the crags, lay down for a much-needed rest, for the night's terrific work after the travelling, want of food, and strain of the past few days had made her about all in.

That morning, Burton and his son went up on to Blenthorpe to look over the sheep there, but on the northern heath they found none. They were utterly at a loss to account for their disappearance, but when they got on top of the Great Rigg, they could look across on to Wancheate and saw the sheep amongst the crags on the lower breast, and the five ewes that had lost their lambs were back by the beckside searching for them. They could scarcely believe that they could be the missing sheep, for it was almost incredible that they had crossed the beck ; yet they knew that all the sheep had been removed from Todhunter's farm two or three days before, and so, as there should have been no sheep there at all, they went down to investigate.

The Burtons soon saw that they were their sheep, although they could not account for their being there : even if Todhunter had returned, which they thought unlikely, he must have gone out of his mind if he had stolen a whole flock of sheep from the very next fell. They went up to the house and, finding it deserted, they set about driving the sheep back to their own farm, and very little pleased they were at the idea, for to go around by the bridge was a matter of ten or eleven miles. They sent their dogs out and gathered the sheep, which took some time, for they were but moderate dogs, and then started down the track towards Stonethwaite and the bridge.

To watch Parker drive back to Bennet's farm the six wethers that Todhunter and she had stolen from there, had been almost more than Beth could stand, but then she had been far from home and knew well that she had no business to be where she was and so must not show herself. But this was a very different thing, she was on her own farm, and she considered that, now

the sheep were there, they were her own, too :
so, although her dislike of strangers kept her in
the crags and out of sight while the gathering
was going on, as soon as the Burtons started to
drive the sheep off, Beth came down to put a
stop to the rot.

Beth slipped around in front of the sheep and
lay down in the track in their face. The Burtons
swore at her, but she paid not the slightest
attention, indeed, as they did not know or call
her by name, and as she had never taken orders
from anyone but Todhunter, she did not even
suppose that she was being spoken to ; although
she certainly would not have heeded them in any
event. The Burtons continued to drive on, and
manned their two dogs on on the flanks, but
Beth had far the stronger eye so that the sheep,
being compelled to break somewhere, broke
past Burton's weaker-eyed dogs on the flanks.

The Burtons got the sheep together again and
young Burton went round to the front and drove
Beth away. Then they tried to take the sheep
along between them with the two dogs on the
flanks as needed : but all Beth had to do, and
she did it too, was to run in on either flank she
chose and stampede the sheep, who were quite

unable to stand up to her, but broke past whichever they thought the weakest point of the other
four.

It was very plain to the Burtons that, as long
as Beth continued to obstruct them, it was quite
hopeless to think of making any progress, so they
tried to get hold of her, but she simply dodged
back a little way up into the crags, to return once
more as soon as they made any further attempt
to move the sheep.

Burton recognised Beth as the bitch that had
been with Todhunter when they had tried to
search his farm the previous autumn, and, being
thoroughly out of temper, they both went off
to try and borrow a gun from Moore, the falconer,
whose cottage was the nearest, and who they knew
had a gun.   Moore did not like the Burtons, and
he would not lend the gun until he had heard
what they wanted it for, and when they had told
him he refused altogether, for though he did not
know anything about Beth, he disliked the idea
of shooting any dog, and he further told them that
they might well get into trouble with Sir Ian
Stuart if they got shooting dogs on land which
belonged to him and which they did not
rent.

Neither of the Burtons had forgotten the squire's annoyance when they had tried to search Todhunter's farm for stolen sheep ; so, while young Burton went home, the father, after getting some tea with one of his cronies in Stonethwaite, went up to the Manor to ask the squire's permission to shoot or otherwise deal with Beth.

CHAPTER XXIII

URSULA STUART

ALTHOUGH it was early summer, Ian and Ursula Stuart were sitting before a log fire in the big hall at the Manor. Ian had just told the news, which he had first heard that afternoon, that Todhunter's body had been found in the River Sturn.

" Poor John Todhunter," Ursula said, " but perhaps it was the best thing that could have happened : I suppose they must have caught him in time, and prison would have only been a slow death for him. I wonder what became of that dog of his, Beth, do you know if she was drowned, too ? "

" No, I don't know, I heard nothing of any dog."

" What a wonder she must have been ! She must have had an awful lot to do with the stealing if Tatters' story was true, and I suppose

279

it was. Poor Todhunter! it makes you think. You know, only the day before he was arrested, I was out there fishing, and when it came on to rain he lent me his best coat to keep me dry on the way home, and I never took it back either; but he —he won't need it now, will he ? What a shame it all is! I wonder what on earth made him start stealing ? "

" I don't know, Urs'la, I'm sure, but I never thought the fellow was quite right in his head myself, and perhaps that is the kindest thing to think."

The butler entered to announce Burton.

" Shall I have him in here." Ian asked, " or would you rather not ? "

" Oh, yes, I don't mind," and as the butler went out: " I'm afraid he knows I don't like him, so it'll look better anyway."

Burton came in and told his story, but omitted to mention that he had tried to borrow Moore's gun. Ian asked a few questions, but Ursula said nothing: she sat still, looking into the wood flames and gently rubbing the ears of an old, pensioned, rheumaticky deerhound that was sitting with his head in her lap. Presently she forgot that she was in her own hall at the Manor, and she

began to see in fancy in the flickering flames
pictures of Beth:

Beth coming home the long, weary miles
southwards across the border from the River
Sturn, for she must have gone with Todhunter,
else she would not have allowed the sheep to be
driven away in the first place.

Beth setting out in the dark, alone, to steal
sheep for the master that she would never see
again, driving the great mob down the screes off
the Great Rigg and across the Scarsdale Beck.
How, how in the world had she ever done that?

And Beth lying up in the crags, ready to come
down to guard her stolen sheep against all
comers.

At the shining loyalty of it a lump rose in
Ursula's throat till it almost choked her, and her
eyes began to smart. She came back with a jerk
to the present in time to hear Burton repeat his
request for permission to shoot Beth, and for the
first time entering into the conversation she
said:

" Oh, you wouldn't shoot her, Ian: you
couldn't do that! "

" No, of course not, if it can possibly be avoided;
but Mr. Burton must have his sheep, and anyway,

unless we can get hold of her, if we leave her out loose she will sooner or later take to lamb-worrying or something—she'll have to live: goodness knows how she has kept herself all this time. Do you think you might get hold of her, Urs'la ? Perhaps she knows you a little as you were so often there."

" I'll try, but I'm afraid there's not much chance, for all those Fly breed were shy—Beth's out of Fly, you know—and Meg was the only one who would ever pay any attention to me: besides, lately I've hardly seen Beth, since they started —well, lately."

" She'ld never come till the', m'Lady," said Burton. " She's t'wildest beggar I ever see, and she's ne good for owt, all she did de was te flate me sheep."

Ursula did not bother to reply, for she thought that a dog that could bring three hundred sheep, many of them ewes with their lambs, across the Scarsdale Beck singlehanded and in the dark, needed no champion in her or anyone else.

Turning to Burton, Ian said:

" I'll meet you at Wancheate Farm at noon to-morrow, if you like, and we'll see what can be done. I can't make it earlier, for I have promised to see Mr. Jackson about his sheepfold in Rowan-tree Gill at half-past nine."

" Yon will ne gie us ower-much time te fetch t'sheep yame afore dark, Sir Ian; 'tis a canny long way all around be t'brig."

" Well, if you like, make it Wednesday, earlier in the morning, but I must see about the fold to-morrow, I arranged it with Mr. Jackson some days ago. And if the dog is shot on my land, I'll do it myself, remember that."

" Verra good, Sir Ian, I'll be waiting till the' at Wancheate at noon temorrer."

" Right, that's settled, then."

" Good night, Sir Ian."

" Good night."

" Good night, Mr. Burton."

" Good night, m'Lady."

The next morning no more was said about Beth. Ian was in a hurry to get off as he wanted to see Bellis about one of the deerhounds before he was to meet Jackson; and Ursula was late for breakfast as usual and did not get down till Ian was just off.

As soon as she had finished her breakfast Ursula set off for Wancheate. As a rule, when going any distance, she rode or drove, but to-day she walked, for if she could by any chance get hold of Beth, she thought that she would be more ready to follow her on foot than riding or driving. She took Todhunter's coat and a whistle which Todhunter had made her and which she had always used when trying to work Meg, and she stuffed a pocket with bits of biscuit, though she had little faith in the biscuit doing any good, for Beth was not likely to be influenced much by anyone simply for food.

Before Ursula had covered the first two of the four miles that separated Wancheate from the Manor it had begun to rain, not very hard, but nevertheless a steady, soaking rain. She thought that Todhunter's coat was likely to be her strongest card, so she would not put it on and get it wet, but only rolled it into a tighter bundle and thrust it closer beneath her arm. As she came up the track to the farm she saw the sheep grazing, but no sign of Beth. She went on into the yard and there tied the coat loosely by the sleeves around her waist so that it hung inside-out over her skirt almost to the ground. Then she took out her flat tin whistle and blew Todhunter's curlew-like " come-in " note: " whoor-whe, whoor-whe," a pause, and then again, " whoor-whe, whoor-whe."

Beth, up in the crags, was sleeping the dead sleep of the utterly worn out. The first " whoor-whe, whoor-whe " struck faintly across her sleep, so that she awoke but was not aware what it was that had woke her ; she must have just heard the tail-end, though, as she awoke, for she stood staring about her, quite certain that something most terribly important had happened but unable to think quite what.

" Whoor-whe, whoor-whe."

Gone was all Beth's weariness, stiffness and hunger, gone her loneliness and despair, gone as though they had never been. Beth came racing madly down the crags at breakneck speed and, as every ten or fifteen seconds Ursula whistled again, Beth seemed to go even faster than ever. Perhaps Ursula had not quite the same notes as Todhunter used, but it was near enough, and Beth was so frightfully anxious to believe that it was her master that she never for a moment doubted it. She struck a foreleg against a stone and for a moment went lame, but almost at once she went on as well as ever, and she never really felt the pain, her brain was so filled with the great fact that Todhunter had come back that there was no room for anything else.

Between Beth and the farm were twenty or
thirty ewes and lambs feeding pretty close
together: all Beth's instinct and training bade her
go quietly around sheep, but she was not bothering
about any of that now and she raced smash
through the middle of them, scattering them in all
directions, cutting off ewes from their lambs and
even bumping into a lamb that tried to cross her
path to get to its mother and sending it rolling
head over heels. She came skittering around the
corner of the byre into the yard to find not
Todhunter, but Ursula, standing there. She
could have no doubt that it had been Ursula all
along, for at the moment that Beth saw her she
had the whistle in her mouth and was blowing
it.

Beth stopped short, her claws scratching on the
cobbles, and suddenly felt very flat: her first
impulse was to turn and go back to the crags,
but something stopped her: she knew Ursula
pretty well, for whenever she had come to the
farm, Beth had known it, even though Ursula
might not have seen her: she knew that Ursula
appeared to be a friend of Todhunter's and
supposed, therefore, that she must be all right;
besides, the coat made her smell of Todhunter

and Beth thought that there must be some con-
nection; and this last disappointment had knocked
all the fight out of her, she was desperately lonely,
and Ursula seemed the next best to Todhunter.
So Beth lay down and awaited developments.

Ursula called quietly.

" Come on, Beth, Beth lass, Beth, good lass,
Beth, come on, Beth, come on, lass."

But Beth would not move.

Ursula took a couple of paces towards her, but
stopped as Beth lifted her lips to show her gleaming teeth.   Ursula was not a nervous person, but
her surroundings were not such as to inspire much
confidence: the rain fell steadily from the leaden
skies, there was no human being within two or
three miles, and no sound except the rush of the
water in the Wancheate Gill behind the barn, the
drip of the rain from the eaves, the intermittent
and eerie whistling of the curlews, and high overhead from the direction of the Black Crags the
gurgling croak of a questing raven.   Beth's very
silence made her the more unpleasant, and she
looked very wicked as she lay there, her ears flat
on her skull and her teeth gleaming, and Ursula
remembered how she had attacked Peters by the
mongrel trees.

In fact Beth was far more frightened of Ursula than Ursula was of her: she was not in the least savage, only rather shy.

Ursula was not one to walk out four miles to get Beth, and then, when she was within ten yards of her, to go back without her because she was frightened. She gave herself a bit of a shake, told herself that Beth had only attacked Peters because Todhunter had manned her on, and started to walk slowly in towards her, talking quietly the while.

As Ursula came up, Beth never moved but lay tense as a tautened wire, her teeth showing and her eyes fixed anxiously on Ursula's face. Ursula slowly bent down, still talking, and held out her hand, back towards Beth and with the fingers closed, lest anything in the nature of a clutching hand should frighten her. Beth allowed her to gently rub her ears, and then Ursula, forgetful of the filthy yard, sat down beside her, rubbing her ears and talking to her.

Beth dropped her lips over her teeth, and Ursula could feel the tenseness slowly going out of her body; and after what seemed an age, her ears slowly came up and the doubt began to die out of her eyes. Ursula thought that she had won, but she still stopped there talking till suddenly Beth's eyes flickered, her ears flicked back, her jaws opened and—she " laughed."

It was a pitiful effort, but it was enough; Ursula knew that her allegiance was given and would not be withdrawn. She passed her hands down over Beth's ribs for the first time and felt them staring through the skin.

" Oh, poor soul, you're starving. Here, wait a moment," and she dug out the bits of biscuit from her pocket. Beth snaffled the lot as though she had about forgotten what it was like to eat.

Ursula got to her feet saying:

" Come on, lass, I'll find you something better than that when we get home," and turned to leave the yard.

Beth hesitated for a moment and then followed her away, and from that day she never followed anyone else. Ursula walked on up the track with Beth at her heel. Beth stopped as they passed close to some of her stolen sheep, but when Ursula said:

" That'll do, Beth, never mind them, come on, lass."   Beth followed her on.

They did not have to pass through Stonethwaite but went through the back gates, which had on

one pillar an excellent carving of a fell hound,
sitting on his haunches with his nose in the air,
apparently hardly winding the carven fox on the
other pillar a few yards in front of his nose: the
fox was facing the hound and, from his attitude,
evidently intended to make a fight of it as soon
as the hound should cease to bother about his
exceedingly moderate nose and deign to use his
eyes; then across the park and through the beech
coppice where the rookery was, for rooks seem
to be the snobs of the feathered world and always
if possible, even though apparently far from
convenient, they make their nests near to some big
house, as at the Manor, evidently thinking that
nothing less is grand enough for them. The
young rooks were just beginning to fly and there
was great cawing going on, what with old birds
encouraging the young ones and the young ones
calling for help.

As they came through the stableyard Beth
stopped once more and looked anxiously up at
Ursula, as if to ask whether it was all right for
her to come into such a public spot, or if she
should keep out of sight. Ursula called her and
she came quickly up, very much afraid that she
would lose her new and only friend. They went

around to the front and up to the big hall door,
and there Beth had a trying minute with all the
dogs of the place.

Sweep, a big, black, flat-coat retriever, was lying
on the doorstep. As he saw Ursula, he came out
pleasedly and evidently asking for something:
Ursula whipped off her hat and gave it to him,
he took it in his mouth and preceded her proudly
into the house. What he liked best of all was
to take her hand and lead her in somewhat in the
manner of a bridegroom down the aisle of a church,
but to-day Ursula wanted to look to Beth, and so
rather than disappoint Sweep altogether, she gave
him her hat.

As they came into the door they were met by a
whole pack of dogs, tall, stately deerhounds,
proud as the old Scottish kings to whom their
ancestors had belonged; soft-coated, sad-eyed
setters waving their feathery sterns; and little
sharp fell terriers, hot little beggars, brave as
game-cocks, came yapping excitedly at the stranger.
Last of all, old Wings, a fawn English greyhound, the muscles rippling and swelling beneath
her fine skin, skin so fine that the light showed
pinkly through it where it stretched tight between
the hock and the tendon achilles.

Wings' real name was Evening Glory, but no
one remembered that it was, unless they looked
up her pedigree, and Wings herself certainly had
no idea that she had ever had such a name.
Wings was the last remaining evidence of an
attempt of Ian's to course the deer with smooth
English greyhounds as well as the rough Scotch
ones. Wings had not only been the best of the
smooth greyhounds, but the best that Ian had
ever owned or seen: nothing could rival her
matchless speed, style, and game. Though she
weighed but fifty pounds in running condition
in her day, she had run straight up to a royal hart,
struck somewhere about the shoulder or elbow,
and turned him over like a shot rabbit: once
down he never got up again, Wings was at his
throat long before he could find his feet.

She had almost been too good, she went too
hard, and raced over the rough, steep fells, with
their sudden, narrow gills and scattered boulders,
as though they had been the rolling downs of her
native Wiltshire. At the finish she had broken a
foreleg against a stone in the run-up before ever
she came to her hart. That had been the fate of
nearly all of them: they smashed themselves on
the rough ground by their reckless style of going,

one had broken his neck and all of them were for
ever lame with broken toes if nothing worse:
besides, with their thin coats they could not stand
being out for long hours in cold, wet weather, and
they had not enough weight to really stop a hart
if he could keep his feet at the first onslaught.

Wings had been the first that Ian had tried,
and he was so delighted with her brilliant style
that he had got a lot more; but they had not been
a success from their delicacy and lack of weight,
for none of the others had Wings' trick of knocking the hart over in mid-stride: some of them had
not entered readily to deer, and worst of all it
was too sickening to come up and find them
standing trembling with a broken or sprained leg
from the rough ground : there was risk enough
from the hart's horns and feet without the other
as well, and Ian had finally given them up in
favour of the harder and more reliable, if sometimes less brilliant, Scotch greyhound.

When Wings had broken her leg it had been
carefully set and she was pensioned off, for Ian
liked to see her about the place, a living memorial
of her brilliant courses, far better than the mounted
heads of the harts that she had killed, where they
stared glassily down from the walls in the hall.

For a moment, as Beth hesitated at the hall door, there seemed to be every possibility of a fight. Ursula stopped in the doorway and Beth crowded close against her legs, but she was well able to give an account of herself and stood, every hair along her back on end and her teeth showing, silent and prepared. If there was to be a fight the terriers would be the ones to start it, and Ursula kept her eyes on them: one little blue and tan bitch, her face a mass of scars and with cross little eyes, came up spoiling for a fight although Beth was twice her height. Ursula shoved her away with her foot saying:

" Get out of it, Sall, you little devil. If you start fighting, you'll get some wood. I'll give you such a twisting."

Sall retired into the background, still grumbling.

The others came up one by one and introduced themselves to Beth, who stood still and very watchful. She was rather frightened of so many dogs in a strange place, but she was determined to stick to Ursula now at all costs, and her very steadfastness did much to avert the threatened fight.

Presently Ursula walked on into the hall,

talking quietly to Beth the while: Beth still clung close to her legs. Sweep was standing in the middle of the hall still holding Ursula's hat. Ursula took it off him, saying as he gave it up half-unwillingly:

" Yes, I know, Sweep, old man, it's all very well for you, but what would Ian say if he saw ? You know he pays for my hats."

There was a big spot of white saliva where Sweep had been holding it. Ursula smeared it across the brim in an unsuccessful attempt to wipe it off, shook out some of the rain and threw it on to a table, then saying:

" Come on, Beth, let's see what we can find to eat." She went through the back into the kitchen.

She was soon cutting pieces off a fine raw steak and throwing them to Beth, who sat at her feet and caught them before ever they reached the ground. About half the steak had disappeared in this way when the horrified cook came in.

" Gawks on, m'Lady, the grand steak I had till yere suppers! Couldst the' find nowt else te gie t'dog ? "

" Ah, Mrs. Kelly," said Ursula, still vigorously hacking away at the steak, " you'll find something for us, I'm sure, and poor Beth's so hungry."

Beth ate the whole of the steak and was looking around for more, but Ursula thought that she had had enough and went up to change her wet clothes. Beth followed her about like a shadow and was lying at her feet, indeed against her feet, when Ian came in.

" Well, that was a fine wild-goose chase; there was no dog at all, and Burton took his sheep away without hindrance from anyone."

" Oh, I'm so sorry, Ian. I never thought of you going all the way out there. I went and fetched her, and here she is," pointing over the side of her chair, where Beth, who had got up as Ian came in, was looking anxiously around her legs.

Ian walked up, but Beth, who was still a little shy, slipped round the back of the chair and came up on the other side of Ursula's legs.

" All right, old girl," Ian said, " I won't bother you. How did you get her, Urs'la ? "

" I went out into the yard at Wancheate and blew Todhunter's whistle—you know, I've got one—and after a minute Beth came tearing into the yard. Oh, Ian, I could have wept: I never saw anyone look so lost. You could see she thought it was Todhunter whistling and when

she saw me instead, she pulled up short and stood
for a moment looking at me, and she seemed to
sort of grow smaller, she had been so frightfully
pleased and then she was so disappointed.   It was
a mean trick to play on her, but she would never
have come to me otherwise.   She wouldn't come
any closer, but lay down, so I went up to her, and
after a little she seemed to make up her mind I
was better than nothing, and followed me home.
I was afraid of a fight when we came in—that
little brute Sall was the worst—but it was all
right and Beth sticks to me like a limpet.   Poor
little soul, I expect she has had enough of being
lost."

CHAPTER XXIV

SHEEP ONCE MORE

For days Beth never left Ursula's side; she slept with her and followed her about everywhere, even going into the very bathroom. She did not like other people to touch her at first and Ursula took care that no one bothered her.

Ursula was rather afraid of how Beth would behave with her first-born, Peggy; the heir to the house of Stuart, Peter, was not yet of an age to walk about, so he could not get into trouble. But her fears were groundless for Beth was only shy, and that largely because she had scarcely ever seen anyone but Todhunter; and she was wise enough to appreciate that Peggy was Ursula's ewe lamb, and she was good to her, and indeed she let her touch and pat her before she would allow anyone else. She took to Ian pretty well in a few days but never cared for any of the servants, and the dislike there was mutual. She never followed anyone but Ursula and never took food off anyone else, though if Ursula was out at feeding time, Beth would eat up if the food was put down for her and left.

At first Ursula let Beth go everywhere with her, but after a while, when she was settled down a bit, she made her stay at home when bidden. Beth obeyed all right but looked so unhappy that Ursula, who rarely went anywhere where it was impossible to take a dog, usually allowed Beth to go everywhere with her.

The trouble was that Beth could not forget the loss of Todhunter: it was not that she mourned him after once she had taken to Ursula, but she was always afraid of being lost again, and was terrified to let Ursula out of her sight. She even went to church, but not in it: she would lie in the churchyard during the service, in hot or wet weather beneath an aged yew that in its time had grown many a good longbow. Beth soon learnt to recognise the music which heralded the end of the service, and would get up from under her tree, yawn and stretch, and walk over to the door to wait till Ursula should come out.

Ursula did not worry a great deal over Beth at church, for she had enough trouble with her own

Peggy, who had just started going to church and was of that age which likes to enliven what it considers a dull entertainment. Ursula would not easily forget her shame when Peggy, between the Manor and the church, managed to secrete about her small person two large snails, which she proceeded to liberate and race during the Litany. One of them turned out to be a bit of a flyer, and got out of control, wandering out of her reach towards the aisle. At last it got into the aisle, and became there the admired of all beholders. Ian was sitting on the outside and, as Ursula believed, connived at, if he did not actually abet, the snail race. Ursula, who was sitting on the inside, could not reach or retrieve the snail.

By the time that the collection was taken the snail had reached the very middle of the aisle, and had been seen by almost everyone except the stout, sleek, and very pompous haberdasher Snook, who, with nose in the air, was carrying the offertory plate before him as though he were a flunkey with a boar's head at the very least. It was therefore made infinitely the funnier by anticipation when Mr. Herbert Snook trod heavily upon the recent winner of the snail Derby and skidded miles across the stone floor, the collection flying in all directions and the silver salver falling on the flags with a clang that could be heard to the end of the village street.

Beth had a very good, if lazy, time at her new home. Ursula went a good deal fishing and Beth would lie down quietly, watching her or the little sleek dippers, looking with their white waistcoats exactly like fat family butlers. Beth was always rather surprised to see them looking for food, when they would run down off a stone into the water and completely disappear for quite a little while as they ran about on the bottom, and then run up out of the water on to the stone again. Ursula liked to watch the birds and animals on the fells, and Beth never got in the way, for when Ursula wanted to stop unnoticed, Beth would always lie down and keep still when bidden.

Some time after Ursula had had Beth, and when she felt that Beth had taken well to her, she thought that she would like to see her work. She knew Todhunter's whistles and, knowing what a good one Beth must be, she did not anticipate any great difficulty.

Ursula had no sheep of her own save an old ewe that had been given to her as a pet lamb, and a very great nuisance she had since become; she was completely boss of everyone and could get through or around almost any fence and was for ever getting into the garden and eating the most precious plants. Indeed, if it had not been for Ursula, who still retained a sneaking affection for her once pretty pet lamb, the tiresome old ewe would have long since been mutton. An effort had once been made to return her to Jackson from whom she had originally come: but the old lady far preferred the rose garden to the fell and was back within twenty-four hours; so Ian and the gardeners could now only hope for her early decease.

The pet lamb had, curiously enough, struck up a great friendship with Peggy's donkey, which friendship was wholeheartedly returned by the ass. In her second summer Ursula had thought that her pet looked hot, and she was accordingly clipped. After the clipping the donkey for some time failed to recognise his friend and would have nothing to do with her, but was in a frightful state of mind and searched everywhere for what was under his very nose, and in fact actually for once lived up to the quite undeserved reputation of his race for foolishness.

Even more peculiar than the friendship between the donkey and the ewe was one between a dog and a raven: a farmer in St. Johns-in-the-Vale had a big sable dog, Toss, who, though a noisy barking sort of animal, might have been a very useful sheepdog if he had had a real chance, for he was very wise.   He never did much work but lived loose about the farm, indeed his only regular job was to fetch in the cows for milking in the summer when they were out at pasture; and, although the milking cows usually ran with a fair number of heifers and dry cows, Toss never brought in any but those in milk.   Of course, Toss could not tell a cow in milk from a dry one, but he could tell those cows which were being milked, and he rarely made a mistake twice, though the business was easier than it sounds, as the milking cows had an idea about going away into the byre at milking times which the dry ones had not.

One day Toss's owner brought home a young raven, and he and Toss at once took to each other. After a while, when the raven was grown and had his powers of flight, he learnt to go to the village and steal pieces of meat from the butcher, and he could take fair-sized pieces, for the raven is a powerful bird. But such was his friendship for Toss that after stealing the meat he would allow Toss to take it off him: and Toss and the raven used to make combined, and most unpopular, raids on the village, the raven stealing the meat which Toss ate, or at any rate a great deal of it; and probably the raven stole for sheer mischief's sake. He, or perhaps she, had a sort of nest in the angle made between the chimney and the roof of his owner's farm, and there he collected an enormous quantity of miscellaneous articles which took his fancy, spoons, knives, bits of paper, articles of clothing, broken crockery, and good-ness knows what else; and his owner was forced to make periodical raids on the nest with a ladder to retrieve any valuable property that might be there.

As the pet ewe could scarcely have been of much use to Beth, Ursula went over to Jackson's farm to ask his permission to work Beth on some of his sheep.

Jackson was looking over some sheep that had done poorly on the fell and had with him an old white dog, Jaff. Jaff, who, though called white, had several black patches on him, was a rather remarkable old dog. He would work for Jackson, but for no one else ; there was nothing very remarkable in that.   Indeed, it is the general rule for dogs only to work for their master: but Jaff would work for Jackson by deputy.   One of Jackson's sons had a farm a little way from his father's, and he often borrowed Jaff.   If he simply took Jaff out, Jaff might follow him if he was bored with being shut up, but he very likely would not work for him.   Yet if Jackson took him out and said to his son in Jaff's hearing :

" Shout to Jaff, Tom, shout to Jaff," and the son then called Jaff, he would go with him and work his best all day, for he thought that it was his master's wish.   But the next day he would not go with him unless old Jackson were to say again, " Shout to Jaff "; yet if Jackson ordered him in that way, he would do his best for the veriest stranger.   Jaff had another useful trick, for he would point to a maggoty sheep.   He could wind one at a great distance, which was perhaps feeling bad and had lain down under a stone, or in a scrape, or somewhere where it might easily be missed.   Jaff would point it like a pointer on grouse, and when encouraged would walk up to it and show where it was.

Jackson readily agreed for Ursula to try Beth,

and as he was busy himself he offered to send his son with her, but Ursula said she would not bother him, so Jackson told her to go anywhere and do anything she pleased on the fell.

Ursula went a little way up the fell and presently saw ten or a dozen sheep about three hundred yards away. She had scarcely said the " Beth " of " Beth, go-o 'way," before Beth was away like a flash. She made a beautiful outrun very fast and wide, and got hold of her sheep at once; then she brought them up quickly and quietly in her own inimitable style.

Ursula was delighted and, when the sheep were within a hundred yards of her, she thought to twist Beth about a bit. She gave the right whistle, " whe-whew, whe-whew," but to her astonishment Beth took not the slightest notice; she whistled again louder, but still no effect. Then she gave the stop whistle, " whiew." But Beth still brought the sheep on straight towards Ursula, who at last tried the voice. " Go down, Beth, go down," but still Beth brought them on.

The sheep were now right up to Ursula and Beth watched that they did not go to the right or left of her: the next moment and they went by her, almost equally divided half to the right and half to the left.　In a flash Beth had raced round in a wide sweep and held them back once more. Ursula whistled and spoke sharply to Beth, but still she brought them on until they had broken past Ursula again, when once more she raced around and got beyond them.

There was nothing to do.　Ursula turned away, saying:

" That'll do, Beth, that'll do, come in to me."

Beth, seeing her turn her back and walk away, left the sheep and followed her, and Ursula went home, thoroughly disappointed, not with Beth so much as with herself.　She could not think where she had gone wrong: she knew that she had had the whistles pretty well right, and that Beth was a good one; and yet Beth had paid no attention to her, which was the more surprising because Beth was very obviously devoted to her and should have been anxious to please.

However, after a while she began to make allowances in that Beth had done no work for several weeks and so must be a bit hot and excited; and although she knew the whistles and Beth knew her well, yet they had never tried working together before, so that perhaps she had expected too much, especially as Beth's terrific power must make her hard to hold, and her very excellence would tend to make her anxious to hold the sheep up to her handler; and perhaps she would be easier to move when they had had a little practice together.

The result of all her thinking was that Ursula decided to try again the next day and see if they got on any better, but for all that she could not quite get over her disappointment, nor get rid of the idea that Beth could not like her well enough to trouble to obey her.

That night, before she went to bed, Ursula turned all the dogs out of doors as usual, but when she called them in Beth, usually one of the first, was not there: she whistled and called for a long time, and even went out a little to look for her, but she could see nothing in the dark. Finally she went in and, leaving the door open, waited up in the hope that Beth would come in. After an hour's waiting, with periods of calling and whistling, and one or two walks out into the garden and park, Ursula, though still worried, gave up and went to bed.

The next morning, being anxious about Beth,

Ursula got up early to look for her. She had not far to look, for Beth was lying beyond the garden fence, farther than which she could not bring them, with the sheep of Jackson's, which the day before she had been sent to gather and which in the night she had gone and stolen.